Do You Want Monkey Blood With That?

With That?

By Ron Clarke

First Published in 2022 by Blossom Spring
Publishing
Do You Want Monkey Blood With That? ©
2022 Ron Clarke
ISBN 978-1-7396277-6-8
E: admin@blossomspringpublishing.com
W: www.blossomspringpublishing.com
Published in the United Kingdom. All rights
reserved under International Copyright Law.

Do You Want Monkey Blood With That? Is dedicated to the good people of Northumberland. Their humour, generosity of spirit and wonderful dialect, never fails to light up even the darkest of days.
Some names have been changed in genuine care and as a gesture of goodwill. They looked after me in my younger days.

About the Author

Ron Clarke was born in Newcastle and graduated with an honours degree in Sociology and Politics from the University of Bradford.

Always interested in writing, he got a job as a reporter with the weekly Harrogate Advertiser newspaper, covering everything from the opening of care homes to the Eurovision Song Contest. He then stepped up to daily reporting with the Halifax Evening Courier.

He later returned to his native North East as a Press Officer with Northumbria Police, before becoming a Communications Officer for Northumberland County Council. He was then fortunate to land a plum job as PR Manager for Northumberland Tourism, organising itineraries for visiting journalists and showcasing England's most northerly county to the rest of the world.

Several freelance roles followed, including compiling match reports as a football reporter for the Sunday Times for several seasons.

Do You Want Monkey Blood With That? is Ron's debut book published through Blossom Spring Publishing.

Do You Want Monkey Blood With That?

Do you want Monkey Blood with that? Now there's a question you have probably never been asked. Spare a thought for me then. It is something I must repeat at least thirty times a day. Not counting the times I should have asked but couldn't really be bothered. Too much mess. Too sticky.

But here I am posing the same riddle again. This time to a tiny young girl who has decided to venture across the deserted beach even though granite skies are lowered across the sands and the biting wind is getting stronger. Add in the constant rain and there it is, a typical summer's day on the North East coast.

Well that is not actually very fair. In a bored moment I did do some weather research. Yes, this does get a bit lonely sometimes. Did you know that this part of the world,

Northumberland, has more sunnier and drier days a year than Cornwall? Well I think that's right. To be fair such a dull day as this seems to be more the exception than the rule. The last few weeks have brought almost unbroken sunshine and some wonderfully high temperatures. It is going to be one of the hottest summers for years.

This is all great news as I drive an ice-cream van. Well, not entirely accurate as it tends to be more stationary than mobile. I only really make short trips. Like today. Here I am again, nestled close to the harbour with uninterrupted views of the vast curved beach.

Well, at least it was uninterrupted until I got an unlikely visitor for the first time in about an hour. She arrived just I had settled in the driving seat with a good book. Trainers off and feet on the steering wheel. Bliss, pure bliss.

The book of course is an international bestseller. Just how they know this is always a bit of a mystery. This one has just been published. What happens if it turns out not to be? Will they hastily recall and erase the words bestseller from the cover? All a bit embarrassing.

It is described as real page turner. A book you simply can't put down. A bit like The History of Glue as Tommy Cooper once so humorously told us. As for being a page turner it is too early to say. Business has been so brisk recently that not many have been turned. Today was the day supposedly set aside for turning.

Not now as I have some little fingers tapping at the window. I just thought it was a bit of rain dropping through the roof; after all the van is supposedly one of the oldest in the country. Gear stick on the steering wheel, indicators that spring out like arrows and no heating. In fact there should really be a man walking in front of it with a red flag every time I take to the road. It is that old.

Taking to the road is actually a bit of lottery as I never really know if I will ever get to where I am supposed to be going. A bit like life really.

The van has broken down at least three times this summer and been forlornly towed back to the garage. After the holidays I may suggest it could be an interesting item for a vintage vehicle auction.

"Would you like to know how much it is worth?"

"Yes please."

"In its present condition I would have to say worthless, although you might get a few pounds scrap value."

"Wow, that's amazing. I never thought it was actually worth nothing. I am really glad I brought it along now. Thank you very much."

Anyhow, I digress, where was I? Oh yes, back at the tap on the window. Shuffling to my feet, putting the book down, I eventually manage to get across and slide it open. The strong wind and rain is a bit of a shock to the system.

"Yes, can I help you?"

"Can I have a 99 please?"

To those who have not sworn allegiance to

the secret world of ice-cream, this is a cone with a dollop or two of ice cream, topped off with a chocolate flake. Why is it called a 99? Don't ask me. It is just one of the many mysteries of the universe. Just like why BBC Two television programmes always start at least two minutes behind schedule. It is just one of those things we will never know, though there is probably someone out there who does know. Personally, who cares?

But there you have it and there you go. Without trying to sound too shocked as to why someone would want something so cold on such a cold day, I go into automatic mode. Dip down into what is mockingly referred to as the freezer and take out two scoops from the milk churn like storage and carefully place them on top of the cone.

After adding the flake and handing it over I notice she is carefully eyeing the plastic bottle of gooey red liquid. Oh no, she has spotted it. There is no turning back now. My fault really as I had ample time to store it out of sight. I suppose it was just habit that I had placed the plastic bottle in full view and within easy reach.

So here we go.

"Do you want Monkey Blood with that?"

"Yes please." And with a couple of gentle squeezes out comes the gory red fluid. It looks like I have just badly cut my hand and blood is oozing out. It is that horrible, but hey ho, almost everyone seems to like it, apart from me. After swirling it around the top of the 99 it has gone past the flake, past the ice cream, down the cone and onto my hands before I have had time to even hand it over to the customer. What a mess.

"How much is that?" I am so surprised by the whole exchange that I can't even be bothered to charge for it.

"Nothing. It is a one-off special offer. Have a good day."

Off she toddles, clasping the purchase as though it might break and skips away. At least someone is happy.

So why is it called Monkey Blood? Don't ask me, I'm only the organ grinder. Anyway you have probably had enough questions. Let's leave the answer until another sunny day shall we.

The rest of the day passes with barely another sale. A book, the radio and no interruptions. Just how I like it. Well, not really. I am here to make a few bob, have some fun and keep the boss happy. It is turning out to be a great adventure.

These dull interludes are a rarity in what is generally a busy schedule with barely a minute to relax, read or listen to the radio. Well, maybe a slight exaggeration. It is not exactly stressful work and I do have a lot of freedom. I can decide where to go, when to come back and what to do in between—just have to remember how fortunate I am to be doing this.

There must be worse ways to spend your summer break.

***

Probably time for a bit of context. I am an ice-cream man but not all the time. That is pretty obvious. No one is an ice-cream man in this country all the time, are they? Not unless you have the magical formula and can sell the chilled delicacies from a van in the middle of snowstorm in December, when it is only light for about two hours.

No, I am doing this in my spare time, a way of earning money to fund life as a student. Beer is not that cheap you know and as for books, well, I really wouldn't know as I haven't really bought any. Well not the serious research tomes, I prefer a bit of friendly fiction; something to escape away to—keep the mind ticking over, but not so hefty that I should really be taking notes and jotting down references.

I have been to the university library a few times. Mostly to have a chat with friends or pay massive fines for the learned volumes I borrowed months ago and had totally forgotten about. I now need a bit of cash to see me through the summer and maybe some savings for my studies. Burgers aren't that cheap either.

Anyway, enough of that and back to the present. I was lucky enough to land this job through an old school mate who had done it before and foolishly recommended me. I am not entirely sure why he was giving it up. From memory, I think he was about to start a twenty year course to become an architect. Maybe a slight exaggeration but I do know it takes an awful long time to become one. Strangely we kind of lost touch after this. Maybe he is still waiting a few decades to finally graduate.

I do hope he makes it as the brains behind buildings. I owe him a lot. This was his idea, his recommendation and his reference. All it took was a quick phone call, a name check for my pal, and the employment was signed, sealed and delivered. No checking for any criminal records, dubious activities or any interviews.

"*Great. Glad you got in touch. I was looking for a couple of people to help out. Can you drive? Do you have somewhere to stay?*"

"*Yes, fortunately the family have a little touring caravan which no longer tours and has a permanent spot on a site just down the road. I will be staying there and I have passed my driving test.*"

"*Great, the job is yours.*"

As simple as that. Trust on both sides but I think he was taking the bigger gamble. And there really was no training. All of a sudden my entire summer was planned out—didn't really give it a great deal of thought to be honest. Not entirely sure what I had let myself in for. We never discussed wages, hours, training or anything. No forms to fill in, no security checks, no hassle. The job was mine. No turning back.

It was simply a case of turning up on the first day, given a van, told to stock it up and go off and sell; there really wasn't that much more to it. I had never done anything like this before, never sold anything. This was new territory. Any trepidation was soon replaced by anticipation. Looking forward to a summer of fun and a bit of cash along the way.

I had only just passed my driving a test a year ago at the second attempt. The first go was a bit of a disaster. I got through the *"can you read that number plate 75 yards away"* okay but then it was downhill, not literally of course as that would have been a little strange. No I remember doing the reverse round the corner bit and leaving tyre marks on the wet pavement.

The examiner didn't really seem that interested either. The occasional grunt seemed to signal yet another mistake. He had obviously passed his quota for those he had to pass that day already. Everyone else would fail.

He even looked a bit bored. I found out later he had marked me down for going too slow. That can't be right. How can you go too slow on a driving test? Breaking the speed limit and hurtling along at 70mph outside a school and near shops I can understand. It looked like yet another excuse to get me out of the car as quick as possible, as he obviously had other more important things to do. Maybe a round of golf, a trip to the local pub or getting home for his tea. Who knows what went through his mind that day to mark me down.

The finale came with the Highway Code section.

He said: *"Now I have to ask you some questions. Not that it is really worth it."* Knowing your speed limits when there are lampposts about and identifying variety of road signs was obviously immaterial as far as he was concerned. He casually flipped open a dog-eared file of various signs and asked me what they all meant. By this stage he could barely stifle a yawn; talk about going through the motions. This was as pointless as it gets. I hope he slept well that night. I didn't. Aside from Newcastle United losing to non-league Hereford in the FA Cup it was one of my biggest disappointments to date.

I remember walking home. Every car that passed me was just adding insult to injury. How I would love to be one of those drivers. It was a long walk and all the time I was thinking about my examiner and what he was doing now. Probably behind the wheel of his own car, driving far too slowly, leaving tyre marks on various pavements and ignoring signs as he didn't know what they meant. Anyhow, how does somebody become a driving test examiner? No sense of humour or communication skills required.

I have since read that those drivers who pass their test at the second attempt are among the safest on the roads. Not sure how they know that but that will do for me. Especially as I have now been given sole custody of an ice-cream van which no doubt I will have to manoeuvre around narrow harbours and tight coastal roads.

Looking back, driving too slow in the test should have been a huge tick for this job.

Never any danger of getting this old van in the fast lane. It only has two speeds. Slow and even slower. But it suits me. It fits in with the gentle carefree pace of life around here in the glorious summer days. Anyhow what would be the point of having a van finely tuned to be in pole position in a Formula One race. I am selling ice cream and stopping and parking, that's about as tactical as it gets.

As someone who enjoys his own company, a bit of a laugh and not too much hard work, this job ticks all the boxes. I like a good book, a bit of Bob Dylan and sport of course. By birth I have been doomed to watch Newcastle United. This far outpost of the country has somewhat bafflingly been described as the hotbed of football. In my life it has been more like a water bed as I have drowned in the continuous flow of disappointment.

It is all down to my Dad. I can vividly remember as a young boy being perched on his shoulders at the back of the terracing at St James' Park. The green grass, the colours and the crowd. I spent most of the afternoon gazing at the sea of humanity gently cascading across the concrete steps. I was hooked.

I have stood on the terracing in virtually all parts of the famous old ground. Starting with the Popular Side, moving to the Gallowgate End, a brief flurry with the covered Leazes End where all the songs come from and then the more sedate wing or central paddocks.

Standing just in front of a crush barrier was the optimum position or sitting on one was even better. This way you could witness all the surges without being involved. In those early days there were white coated men carrying neatly coned paper bags of peanuts circulating around the cinder track next to the pitch. They shouted "tanner a bag" and you threw a coin down and they projected a bag back in your general direction. Sometimes this seemed more entertaining than the game itself.

I suppose I was lured in by a false sense of optimism as a young schoolboy I was lucky enough to see many of the games in the Inter

Cities Fairs Cup in the 1968/69 season. This was a whirlwind introduction into European football with the likes of Feyenoord, Sporting Lisbon and Victoria Setubal coming to St James'. We even managed to lift the trophy with a victory over the Hungarians Ujpest Dozsa in a two-legged final. We led three-nil from the home leg and then conceded two goals before half-time in the second part in Hungary.

Apparently, Manager Joe Harvey, cigarette in hand, said to his players *"just go out score a goal and they will crumble."* And this is exactly what happened. We quickly got one back, followed by two more and cruised to a 6-2 aggregate victory.

We got to the final by beating the mighty Glasgow Rangers. My Scottish father obviously had some great foresight and did not allow me to go. He said I was too young and it might not be a nice place to be. How right he was. The game was almost abandoned as the visiting fans, obviously offended to be losing the contest, decided to invade the pitch in a futile attempt to have the match abandoned. They were met at the half-way line by a ring of police with dogs on long leashes and order was restored.

The sound of sirens filled the night air in Newcastle. It was obviously a busy time for emergency services.

My father, knowing I was desperate to taste the atmosphere, did take me in his car for a tour around the streets next to the ground and quickly back to the safety of home before kick-off. My vivid memory is a Rangers fan, clad in a red, white and blue scarf and hat, standing and waiting for the turnstiles to open. He was clutching one of those big party cans of beer, which probably contained at least five pints, and was drinking it all himself. I guess it wasn't his first and he probably didn't remember much of the game.

Then about two days later I was with my Dad again and he was filling the car up at a petrol station. Alongside the pump in front was a large and fairly dilapidated mini-bus. When the back doors opened about three guys, all attired in Rangers' colours, fell out the back. They had been drinking in the occasion and were just making their way home.

So I thought winning trophies was routine. Obviously not. Rare or even non-existent would be a fairer description as the Fairs Cup turned out not be the start of the fairy tale. I have been to Wembley twice. A couple of years ago we were demolished 3-0 in the FA Cup Final by a rampant Liverpool. As they say we were lucky to get nil. The nets at the national stadium seem so much bigger than any other ground, when the ball lands there it is all in slow motion; the ball just seems to stay still as the net ripples. Seeing this three times was enough to give me motion sickness.

Getting there and back was more exciting than the game. Me and a couple of teenage pals joined the hundreds of fans at Newcastle Central Station waiting to board the football specials that were leaving at around midnight, for the big journey south. The noise reverberating off the huge concave roof was thunderous. On board the train we were in a compartment alongside a dad with his young son and we never really got to open our casually stored bottles of Newcastle Brown Ale. It didn't seem right and anyhow it is a pretty difficult drink, all a bit too murky and powerful for us young ones.

One of my friends had an aunt who lived near Wembley and we went there for breakfast and watched about three hours of the big build-on on the BBC before making our pilgrimage to the home of football. We had to pinch ourselves we were actually going.

The journey back was a real sombre affair. Again I seem to think the train left King's Cross at about midnight and deposited us back in Newcastle in the early hours of the morning. In our compartment was a man who seemed to revel in just how bad our football team had been. We already knew that and a reminder was the last thing we needed. I quickly fell asleep and only woke up as the train slowed down across the Tyne Bridge.

I walked home, at least five miles, passing the piles of stringed up bundles of newspapers waiting outside various newsagents. I did pick up a couple of newspapers and the headlines were all highly critical of the big event which had become a big letdown. I didn't read the words. I already knew the story.

Things got only slightly better this year, 1976, as we lost by the odd goal in three to an incredibly lucky Man City. On any other day the overhead kick winning goal from Dennis Tueart would have landed nearer the moon. Not this time and so the wait for a trophy goes on. I witnessed it all from a prime seat next to the famous steps where the players go up to receive the trophy and then clamber back down onto the pitch for a lap of honour. I was in touching distance. Once again it was in opposition hands.

Back to the Future

Back to the future. My home patch for this hottest of summers is the delightful seaside hamlet of Beadnell right here on the Northumberland coast. Interesting facts you may or may not want to know. It has the only west-facing harbour entrance on the east coast of England and has a population of somewhere just below six hundred. In these summer months it multiplies many times. Many of the houses are sought after second homes or holiday rentals and there are also two large caravan sites just behind the dunes and a much smaller one, which is my temporary home, near the centre of the village. There is also a large camp site, a pub, a local shop and a couple of small hotels.

In the summer it seems that most of Newcastle, migrates some fifty miles to up here, to enjoy the seaside.

There are still a handful of fishing boats with

lobsters and crabs, the main catches of the day. More facts for you. On the harbour are limekilns which are said to have been built around 1789 or so, not really quite sure but I know they are really old.

John Wood, from whose estate the coal and limestone was extracted, would in return keep the harbour in good repair. The original kiln was expected to produce at least one thousand cartloads of lime each year to be transported by sea to various ports in England and Scotland; the lime sold so well that the good Mr Wood built two more kilns on the harbour. The coal and the limestone were brought to the top of the kilns on a tramway. Each kiln was filled from the top with alternate layers of limestone and coal. The burnt lime made quicklime which was said to be used as a fertiliser and in building mortar. They were later used for curing herring and now they are used as storage for lobster pots and a great place for the local fisher folk to sit and natter away to unsuspecting passers-by.

Beadnell is an ancient settlement, the name possibly deriving from Bede's Hall and Bronze Age burials have been found along the shore. Other older activities around here in days gone by included smuggling, horse racing on the beach and coal-mining. Watching the horses would have been good fun today—also good for ice cream sales as I'm sure there would be big crowds.

There is also the site of an 18th century chapel on a rocky outlet and one of the public houses contains a 16th century Pele house. The beach is two miles long and is home for a nationally important colony of Little Terns.

I say facts. It is just what people have told me or what I have picked up wandering around the place and looking at those various history boards which most people never really bother to read. So, if I am wrong somewhere, don't blame me.

If you go up the coast two miles you come to Seahouses. This is where tourism really gets serious. There are schools of fish and chip shops, well at least three, an amusement arcade, gift outlets, cafes, a milk bar, assorted shops, hotels, a huge caravan site, another harbour, a lifeboat station.

I just thought, a school, is a clever collective term for fish and chip outlets.

The seaside and fish and chips go together like a horse and carriage to misquote Frank Sinatra. They always taste that much better with the smell of seaweed and the sound of seagulls in the air. The saying goes that you should never eat fish and chips if you can't see the sea; they are a classic double act but who put the two together is still a mystery. Probably safe to say it was somewhere in England, but north or south? Still a matter of controversy but they are the staple diet of the British seaside.

Some give credit a northern entrepreneur called John Lees. As early as 1863, it is believed he was selling fish and chips out of a wooden hut at Mossley market in industrial Lancashire. Others claim the first combined fish and chip shop was actually opened by a Jewish immigrant, Joseph Malin, within the sound of Bow Bells in East London around 1860. Outlets sprung up across the country and soon they were as much a part of Victorian England as steam trains and smog.

Winston Churchill described fish and chips as good companions and during the Second World War there were strenuous efforts made to make sure they were one of the foods never rationed.

George Orwell in 'The Road to Wigan Pier' (1937) put fish and chips first among the home comforts that helped keep the masses happy and "*averted revolution*".

They have to be wrapped in old newspapers and eaten with greasy fingers for the true experience. And you have to be bombarded with questions. *Cod or haddock? Salt and vinegar? Mushy peas? Wrapped or open?*

There is also a rumour that chips were invented as a substitute for fish. When supplies were limited, resourceful housewives used to cut potatoes into fishy shapes and fry them as an alternative.

They are also the source of one of my favourite lines.

Man walks into a fish and chip shop and asks for fish and chips twice.

The girl behind the counter says: "No problem, I heard you the first time."

The all-important gift shop is just the place to buy a tea towel with Puffins or a jigsaw of the Northumberland coast. People on holiday always like to buy souvenirs that will probably never see the light of day when they get home. It is just something you have to do. Part of the ritual of the annual summer break.

That's probably enough about Seahouses for now. Not quite Blackpool but that's how we like it round here.

Travel a bit further north and you come to Bamburgh, another tiny village, but this one is dominated by one of the most spectacular coastal castles anywhere in the country, if not the entire globe—it is that stunning. It is perched on a rocky outcrop overseeing all that goes on. You can't miss it and it is a wonderful entrance or exit to this most picturesque of places.

The publicity speak tells you that the battlements have stood from an Anglo-Saxon citadel to an impenetrable Norman fortress. It has also been the home to a succession of Kings from Henry VI to James 1. The castle is a hugely popular tourist attraction, complete with grand halls, winding stairs and historical artefacts. It is worth a stroll through the highly impressive state rooms, onto the vast King's Hall and into the armoury in the imposing 12th century keep where weapons from days gone by, including crossbows, pikes and muskets, give you a taste of what battles used to be like.

The castle is a much sought-after wedding venue with great backdrops for the photo album and has several private individual and occupied flats. Now there is an address to talk about. *"My home is my castle and all that. You must drop in sometime."*

The Castle has stood guard above the spectacular Northumberland coastline for more than 1,400 years. Perched almost on top of the world, one side overlooks the village and across rolling countryside to the distant Cheviots and the other side eavesdrops on the fantastic beach that has been the setting for many movies—Ivanhoe, Mary Queen of Scots, Robin of Sherwood and Macbeth to name but a few.

The castle has been owned by the Armstrong family since 1894 and they opened it to visitors in the mid-1900s and they continue to stream in large numbers to this day. And another fact, the grounds are one of the most important Anglo-Saxon archaeological sites in the world, regularly turning up hidden gems.

It is also probably the most photographed structure almost anywhere in the country and has been painted by thousands of artists trying to capture the splendid setting and grandeur of the whole place.

I have seen the castle hundreds of times but

it never fails to impress. Approaching from Seahouses it stands guard at the entrance to the village and from the centre of the village you can look back, as it keeps a huge and watchful eye on proceedings. From the sea and the beach it is almost more spectacular, as it rises from the dunes and takes over the landscape.

Folklore recounts the tale of a distressed young Princess in a pink dress throwing herself to her death from the castle ramparts. She had been refused permission to marry the love of her life. On the right night and in the right light her ghost can still be seen. I have never seen her myself. Not even after a few beers.

In the Beginning

This is my first day on my new venture. You will get more of the details later but basically my home base is a caravan in Beadnell, barely two miles from Seahouses, and I do have a car to get there.

After a quick bowl of cereal and a mug of tea, it is off to work I go. I am not in the least bit nervous, which is a little strange as I have never driven an ice cream van, sold an ice cream or met my new summertime colleagues. I have no idea what time I am supposed to arrive, I just know anytime around 9-ish seems acceptable and I have no idea what my routine is—where I am supposed to be going, how much I am required to sell or what hours I am supposed to be on duty. It is all very informal and relaxed, just like my job interview.

As I turn into Seahouses, I suddenly realise this is it. I have signed my summer away and I don't really know what I am doing. Still, who cares, I am just here to enjoy myself and see what happens.

Just at the bottom of main street, well the only street, I quickly glimpse a couple of bright blue and yellow vans and a couple of guys already cleaning them. I park just next to them and notice the boss looking at me. Oh dear, am I in trouble already? Late on my first day? Not dressed properly? Could be for a bit of verbal warning or instant dismissal. Not sure which as the boss, Mr Ice Cream himself, is poker faced and I can't really tell if he is angry or not.

I needn't have worried.

"Good morning. Great to see you. Welcome aboard. Now let's get started. Your van is just inside the yard, the keys are in the ignition, just needs a bit of a clean and then get it stocked up. Looks like another sunny day. Good news for us ice cream men. Lots of sales today. Any questions, just ask. I am never too far away."

"That sounds good. Thanks. When I have cleaned and stocked where do I go?"

"Well that is entirely up to you. Go where you want really. The only rules are don't go where these two go." He points at two fairly elderly men in pristine white coats.

"Meet Frank and Jimmy. Frank has a regular round through all the villages and Jimmy likes to go in and around Bamburgh. There is also another student, he should be turning up soon."

By the way these are not their real names. Just thought it would be best to give them different titles in case I write any words that my upset them. I doubt this will happen.

Anyhow they are really friendly and ready with advice.

"Good to see you. Always good to have someone else around. After we have finished cleaning and getting loaded up we always have a brew so there will time to catch-up later."

"So what do you do Ron?"

"I am a student."

"Surprised to see you up so early then. Thought you guys spent most of the morning

in bed. *Ever sold ice cream before? Sure you will get the hang of it. We are a friendly bunch.*"

The first sight of my van is a bit of a shock. Compared to Frank and Jimmy with their gleaming and spacious vehicles, mine is a lot older, a lot smaller and to be honest, I wasn't convinced it was actually roadworthy.

My boss suddenly appeared behind me.

"*That's it son. That's yours for the summer. A real beauty. She is very old so take good care of her. She has been part of the fleet for years. One of the family. You will have no problems.*"

This was later questioned one day when I filling up with petrol at the local garage. The owner couldn't believe it was still on the road.

"*It is in the garage more times than out. I thought he had got rid of it. Surprised still to see it. Surely it can't have many miles left now. I shudder to think how it has lasted so long. Must be held together by sticky tape. Good luck.*"

I open the door gingerly and get inside for

the first glimpse of my summer office. The driver's seat does seem comfortable, bit worried about the gears being attached to the steering wheel and the general smallness of it all. I am sure I will get used to it. I will have to.

Behind the driving seat are the all-important cold compartments where I guess the ice cream is stored and opposite is a sliding window as the serving hatch. Other than that there not a great deal of space. I have to crouch slightly while standing and there is not a huge gap between the window and the storage.

I can't really complain. It is not a bad office. I could be stuck behind a desk somewhere with boring paperwork and no air conditioning, so this is not bad. I can't really wait to get out on the road and see if it all works.

Having seen the van, met colleagues and been warmly welcomed by one and all, I do feel a little bit apprehensive. This is all starting to feel a bit real. I am here to do a job. I have responsibilities, I also have to feed myself. I am on my own now. No turning back.

The reality is beginning to descend like a dark cloud on an otherwise sunny day. I really should have thought about this more, what is expected, how I am going to live, cook for myself, wash and budget. These are areas I never really explored before readily agreeing to the job with such speed. What if I don't like it, don't sell any ice cream or just want to come home?

So many questions, but you know what, I am not really bothered about the answers. I am sure everything will be fine. This is just the first day and so far so good, but then again I have done no work. That will change soon. I do get the impression that behind the relaxed informality of it all there is a steely determination and sense of good team work that we are all in this together and we are a band of brothers.

The boss appears again. This time with a menu that he sticks to the window. All sorts of different treats on offer. Single cones, double cones, 66's, 99's, nougat wafers, lollies, cans of pop and the dreaded Monkey Blood.

I get the impression that the menu is more of a vague guide rather than a precise manual. Most of it is written in felt tip pen and I guess the prices can change at a moment's notice. Still, it is a good start and I make a mental note of what I will be selling and roughly how much for.

He then hands me a wooden tray with a few coins in.

"This is just to get you started and to make sure you have enough change for the first customers. Put all your money in here and hand it in at the end of the day."

Well that seems pretty simple and basic. It does all seem a bit informal and rough and ready but I am sure it's all tried and tested. The boss doesn't really say very much. Obviously I have got the job because he trusts me and just expects me to sell as much as possible. But there are no targets, no minimum sales, just very matter of fact, as if to say.

"There you are. There's your van. That's what you are selling. That is where you put the money. Just get out there. See you later."

There is not even an itinerary. Just have to hit the road and find the customers. This shouldn't be a difficult task. I am at the seaside and people like ice cream. It is all part of the coastal experience. It is not rocket science.

Let the battle begin.

***

Before we continue with the everyday odyssey of an ice cream man in Northumberland it would appropriate to give you some more background.

I have to confess I have been here before. Not selling the cold confectioneries but as a casual bystander, enjoying many innocent weeks as a regular visitor to this glorious part of the world.

I was lucky enough to spend all my childhood holidays here, never really realising just how fortunate I was. We rented a cottage for four weeks every summer in Beadnell. It was a tiny, whitewashed structure, amusingly named Wits End, and was just like a Tardis. It looked tiny from the outside but once inside there was somehow enough space for me, my two brothers and mum. My eldest brother was not there all the time as he seemed to have summer jobs back home. Working night shift in a bakery comes to mind. Our Dad, hard at work as a vet, normally joined us for a fortnight.

Looking back, he probably quite enjoyed being home alone in Newcastle for a couple of weeks. A nice break from the demands of family life.

Wits End had red gravel at the front, a long and narrow garden at the back and a path running past the front door taking you past the Women's Institute hut. From there it was just a short walk along the road, over a gate into a field taking you to the caravan site and then onto the beach. The accommodation never seemed cramped, even though it had only one bedroom, a lounge, kitchen and a shower. There was always endless food on the table, no matter what the time of day and a tiny television which we all gathered round to watch the first man landing on the moon. More of that in a moment.

I can't even remember where everyone slept. But we all seemed to fit in and get along. Maybe we weren't all there at the same time; the details are lost in the mists of time but it seemed a magical place.

I say Women's Institutes hut because that was one of the signs on the notice board and it did seem to be almost continuously filled with tables selling jams, cakes, flowers and vegetables. For all I know it could also have been the meeting place for the local parish councillors, getting together to talk endlessly about litter, road signs, lighting, bin collections and other worthy subjects of the day. Maybe these meetings were held under the cover of darkness when I wasn't around.

If you left the front door of Wits End, which actually was on the side of the house, and turned left rather than take the path passed the hut, you would pass a few other small houses and then come to the village store.

My two elder brothers took great delight in asking me to nip along and get some bread, milk and other assorted goodies like elbow grease or tartan paint. It amused those behind the counter if no one else.

We seemed to spend endless days on the beach and in the sea. Friends round the corner in another rented cottage had a small boat with a little outboard motor and we seemed to be forever spluttering along the waves. Never went very fast, never went very far, but it all seemed safe and simple. I am sure we had to wear lifejackets but I can't remember ever falling overboard or reaching Norway.

There were also marathon games of football

or cricket, looking in rock pools, racing up and down the dunes, catching tiddlers and crabs off the harbour, and it never seemed to get dark or cold. In fact it seemed light from the moment you got up to the moment you went to bed and we always had that rosy, slightly brown, tan courtesy of buckets of fresh air and sunshine. We were hardly ever indoors.

Strangely I can't really remember buying ice cream from a van. There must have been vans around and I bet the one I am driving today was out and about in those days, I do remember the exhilarating experience of drinking can after can of Creamola Foam. It came in tiny paint-like tins and raspberry, orange or lemon flavours. The contents were made up of hundreds of mini-coloured crystals and by adding water they would erupt like a volcano with liquid lava that had enough sugar to keep you high as kite for days and destroy all teeth. I don't think the legendary fizzy drink was available at your local dentist.

Added to the completely unhealthy diet was

the occasional ice cream soda. Another volcanic like experience by simply adding a dollop of ice cream to a soft drink and watching it bubble and froth. Consuming it involved both a straw and a spoon.

I don't know how my dentures or stomach survived, especially when you add in regular servings of fish and chips. Maybe the fresh air, sunshine and running up and down the dunes burnt it all off. I can't really remember being ill.

Back to the moon landing. Now there's a great story. Forget those conspiracy people who refused to believe it. It was all just made up to make America look good. Not a bit of it. They are the same people who think the earth is flat. All very worrying. I can safely say that on July 20th, 1969, I sat there, as a 13-year-old, and watched it on a tiny flickering black and white television and it was mesmerising. It is still staggering.

Talk about three men in boat. This was three men in a lunar module. Somehow it was whittled down to two as poor old Michael

Collins was left circling the moon while the other two legged it onto the landing craft and made their way down.

Then came the complex scenario about who would be the first to actually set foot on the surface. You can imagine the conversation between Neil Armstrong and Buzz Aldrin.

Neil: "*I was just thinking Buzz, by the way such a great name, as I am nearest the door I may as well hop off first. I have already got a few words put together about what I might say.*"

Buzz: "*Well we could always swap seats.*"

Neil: "*Not really. It would take too long and we haven't really got the time. We will be landing soon. The Eagle has landed and all that.*"

Buzz: "*Okay Neil. That does make sense. Shame I didn't sit in your seat in the first place. It also has a better view. But as you say, we are where we are, so you go first and I will follow you down. Like the line about the Eagle by the way.*"

But I suppose Buzz had an almost bigger claim to fame as he got one back on Neil by having a quick wee on the moon shortly after they landed. Now there's story to tell your mates next time you're standing side by side in a urinal down the local pub.

"Yes, I must say that it much easier than being caught short on the moon I can tell you."

And poor old Neil got his lines mixed up. Apparently, he was supposed to say "that's one step for a man" but missed out the "a" and then followed it with the great quip "one giant leap for mankind."

Not bad Neil. Considering you didn't have much time to rehearse as you were too busy grabbing the window seat next to the door. It is up there with Kenneth Wolstenholme's *"some people are on the pitch, they think it's all over, it is now."* as Geoff Hurst smashed in England's fourth goal and his third in the 1966 World Cup final. Imagine if he had missed. Then what would have Ken said. *"They think it's all over, well it's over the bar."*

That game was watched by 27 million on BBC television and just four million on the opposite channel ITV with Hugh Johns commentating. To his great credit Johns always says everyone can remember the famous words of his opposite number but not the ones he managed to spurt our at the end of such a famous sporting occasion shared by almost the entire country..

For the record his unscripted words were: *"Hurst, he could make it three. He has! That's it, that's it."* Not quite one small step for man but the Eagle had already landed on the BBC.

Strangely, in the early '70s and the early days of under-age drinking in Newcastle, I seem to remember there was a pub called the Man on the Moon and it really did feel like it was from a different planet. I was probably expecting full scale models of the landing module Eagle, stars and stripes flags and continuous loop reels of Buzz and Neil bouncing around in the Sea Of Tranquillity. Instead you had to go down endless stairs into some kind of dark and quite frankly scary dungeon with loud music blasting out and horrible fizzy beer served in plastic glasses.

Mind you it was also the time of long hair, flared trousers and tank tops. Just makes you wonder where such dedicated followers of fashion come from. Does someone in a chic Paris boutique think it's time they had a laugh at the expense of their friends across the channel.

"Let's make them wear ridiculously short jumpers that must be made of the most ludicrous wool possible and must not match and other items of clothes being worn. And they should not have sleeves. That will make English men think they are wearing something cool and different."

"Any ideas for a name? Tank top sounds good. Let's go for it. Even better if they also wear socks and sandals at the same time. Let's go further they should all wear trousers that are just about as wide as the English Channel."

Another quote from the year of the moon landing came from George Best. *"In 1969 I gave up women and alcohol. It was the worst 20 minutes of my life."*

1969 was also the year of peace and love with Janis Joplin, Jimi Hendrix and all in concert at the infamous Woodstock Festival. They were expecting some 50,000 at best but more than 400,000 turned up and most of them can't remember they were there.

It was called Woodstock even though it was forty miles from there on a dairy farm in Bethel, New York. Organisers turned down the Beatles and Bob Dylan which of course was a huge oversight.

Landing in Northumberland

Let's get back to why I am here in Northumberland.

I sell ice cream. It is a holiday job. It is good fun. It is 1976.

Simple as that really. It gets a bit more complicated when we delve into what I actually sell. There are cones and wafers. Some wafers are plain and the rest are nougat. But more of that later.

Sometimes I even pop a chocolate flake in top and call it a 99. Why a 99? Again all will be revealed so just hang fire for a second. Don't forget my van is also stocked with assorted iced lollies and canned and bottled soft drinks.

Jonny's ice cream recipe is that closely guarded secret that only the inner circle and those in the know can divulge. If they did they would probably have to kill you. Possibly a bit brutal, at the very least it would be a severe slap on the wrists, a sworn oath never to tell anyone and remember that loose lips sink ships.

All we do know it involves milk or cream, maybe some sugar and a spice such as vanilla. Simple really. But when it comes to churning milk, cream and the rest it is the Italians who claim to be the best. Not that anyone round here would agree, including me. Seahouses ice cream is the best in my book. I should know as I have tasted and sold enough.

Let's look at Italian ice cream. It is called Gelato and there is some debate if it is actually an ice cream at all. It contains more milk than cream, making it freeze at a lower temperature, and is churned slower than ice-cream. Who really cares? At the end of the day, it tastes really good. There is some rumour that the Romans invented ice cream. During the Roman Empire, Nero Claudius Caesar frequently sent runners into the mountains for snow, which was then flavoured with fruits and juices. Hard to believe I know. I for one have never ventured into the garden in the middle of winter, built a snowman, and then thought I could just put some fruit toppings on those left-over bits for a nice refreshing snack.

It is also said that "cream ice" as it was called, appeared regularly at the table of Charles I during the 17th century.

And then what about 99's. Have you ever wondered why an ice cream with a bit of chocolate stuck on top, is called a 99? I know I said I didn't really care but I do really. It is my job after all.

Irritatingly, my boss here thought it would be very amusing to give punters the opportunity to purchase a full size 99 or go for the cheaper option, a slightly smaller one, and call it a 66.

Very clever but not properly thought through. Yes, it may, and in fact does, generate a lot of sales but there is no thought for people like me. Those in the frontline. Just imagine, apart from the Monkey Blood debacle, what it is like to be asked at least a thousand times a day:

"What is a 66 then?"

Quickly followed by their own witty retort.

"Is it an upside down 99?"

So funny. The temptation is always to say yes and then dump the inverted purchase right on top of the customer's head. But no, a polite response is, just agree and then add, it is just a smaller version of real thing. The customer is always right.

In all my time doing this job no one has ever asked me why a 99 is actually called a 99. Maybe everyone knows apart from me. Hence a little more research.

Cadburys of all people say the origins of the name have been lost in the "mists of time" so what chance I have got. Let's try a few ideas and see if the fog lifts and we can see a little clearer.

You can choose your own favourite. In no particular order.

It was coined in Portobello, Scotland, where Stefano Arcari—who had opened a shop in 1922 at 99 Portobello High Street—would break a large flake in half and stick it in an ice cream. The name, of course, came from the shop's address.

Italian soft ice cream makers working in County Durham in the 1920s decided to incorporate the flake into their ice creams to increase interest and boost sales and devise a memorable name for their innovative creation.

In the days of the monarchy in Italy the King had a specifically chosen guard consisting of 99 men, and subsequently anything really special was known as a '99'.

The name was in honour of the final wave of Italian First World War conscripts, born in 1899 and referred to as 'I Ragazzi del 99', 'the Boys of '99'. In Italy they were held in such high esteem that some streets were named in honour of them. The chocolate flake may have reminded the ice cream sellers of the long dark feather cocked at an angle in the conscripts _Alpini_ Regiment hats.

Or you could just make up your own suggestion. I am sure I told lots of porky pies just to pass the time.

"Oh yes, the name comes after a famous Italian footballer, Roberto de Flakio, who scored 99 goals in one season."

Remember. The customer is always right. Lots of them probably passed the de Flakio football fable to their friends over a quiet beer or even tried to impress their children with their superior ice cream knowledge.

Before I forget, I must mention nougat wafers. I said I would. This is my supreme delicacy. Right off the a la carte menu. One for the discerning palate. It is what it says. A delightful oblong portion of ice cream between two wafers, preferably one plain and the other made of nougat and all topped off with some chocolate round the edges.

It goes down well I can tell you. But you can have too much of a good thing. After a two-week diet that consisted of fish and chips, nougat wafers, cans of Tropical Lilt and beer, I was decidedly ill. Telling the boss, I could not come in due to a decidedly dodgy stomach, was not a career highlight. I just lay in bed all day with severe stomach cramps and regular visits to the gents. Not the best day of the summer.

Lilt is a relatively new addition to the soft drinks market. It is enthusiastically marketed as being inspired by the flavours of the Caribbean. The sparkling drink comes in a brightly coloured can and is supposed to contain real pineapple and grapefruit juice for that 'Totally Tropical Taste'.

I am virtually addicted to it, as though drinking it makes me look cool. And maybe adding something tropical brings a little bit of the Bahamas or Barbados to Beadnell.

But back to reality and I have to face the music. The boss is not happy with my absence.

"I pay you enough son. Surely you can look after yourself and eat properly. Make sure this doesn't happen again. See you tomorrow. And by the way I am docking some of your wages."

My income was wafer thin that week. I had to make up for it.

***

My life feels like a bit of a film set at the moment.

Can't actually believe this is for real. Great scenery, some wonderful characters, quirky plots, twists and turns. Well, maybe I am going over the top a little. Maybe not a Shakespeare tragedy, although there is plenty of *'hubble bubble toil and trouble, fire burn and cauldron bubble'* especially when the van has broken down again or I have large queue of disgruntled customers complaining about high prices.

This job is probably more of a light comedy, with a bit of history here and there. Talking about prices, I do get a Dad who thinks it is hysterical to complain about the cost of a cone in front of his children. It is not funny.

He is one of the boating fraternities in Beadnell with the sailing club nestling just behind the harbour. The lifejacket and the yellow wellingtons are a giveaway. He may as well just wear a t-shirt saying, I am loaded. In that case why does he always quibble? That is probably why he is rich or at least pretends he is. But little does he know that the bigger the moaning, the smaller the portions he gets. One small scoop for man but one giant leap for ice cream man.

I am the winner in all this, as in true Oliver Twist fashion he keeps coming back for more. We have little conversation. If he wants to impress his kids and those waiting in the queue then that it is fine by me. I will just keep counting the pennies as they stack into pounds and the more wages for me. It is all about keeping the customer satisfied.

You have probably guessed I am not a sailor myself. I have messed about in the odd dinghy or two on the odd occasion and I confess it is very exhilarating. The only thing puts me off is the fact you seem to spend more time getting prepared and then putting all the gear away, than you do actually on the sea; it is all a huge effort for such small adventures. I guess there is still time to be convinced. But I do have some, if very limited experience, of life on the water.

At school I was lucky enough to go sailing on the Norfolk Broads a few times. It was a long way from Newcastle but great fun. Sleeping, eating and sailing on a lovely wooden yacht with a crew of mixed ability. It was also highly amusing to watch those people who hired mini motor cruisers for the week. To be in charge you obviously needed a peaked cap, sunglasses and a smart buttoned jacket. This didn't mean you knew what you were doing, you just looked the part.

The manual for these boats must have said 'stay right' and this is what they did as though they were on some kind of road rather than a waterway, where sailing vessels had to navigate the winds and the currents. There were many near misses and many expletives exchanged every time we nearly bumped into one. Then watching them moor was the highlight of the week. Ropes everywhere, buoys floating away, the boat swinging round at right angles to the bank and lots of red faces and shouting. Just wonderful free entertainment.

People watching is an occupational hazard in this job. Whiling away the hours observing human behaviour is a real treat. Look at the family day out on the beach. They seem to come from nowhere like nomadic tribes wandering across the desert. In their hands, on their shoulders and even on their heads, is enough equipment for basic survival for a few weeks, never mind an afternoon. Chairs, blankets, tables, windshields and vast vessels of food. All this is normally carried by the leaders of the packs, usually the mothers, as assorted offspring tag along behind with buckets, spades, footballs, cricket stumps, bats, tennis racquets and kites. The males of the tribe are most likely to be on the golf course, in a boat or at work and may occasionally join later just as the sandwiches are being shared around.

Eating on the beach is never a good idea.

Cheese and tomato, tuna or ham are fairly tasty and traditional sandwiches when consumed indoors, on a bench or in a park. But by the sea they should come with a health warning. That is really putting the sand in sandwich. Every grain seems to get everywhere. It is literally a case of gritting your teeth.

Then we have kites; these should really be blowing in the wind. Not on most days around here when there is hardly a breath and take-off is impossible. Instead of flying like a bird in the sky, the strings are tangled, they rise barely two feet off the ground and land in the distance like a beached whale. Beach dwellers spend more time rescuing the mangled wreckage than flying them. It all seems a bit pointless.

And you can't say would-be kite fliers haven't been warned. There is sign in the gift shop in Seahouses, where the kites fly off the shelves to eager youngsters, stating that no refunds will be given. This is not surprising as they would be quickly returned, probably after the twentieth aborted take-off, battered to bits. The shop doesn't want a queue of disappointed dads and wailing wee ones. Not good for business.

Still, I don't know why I am complaining. I am not involved. I am just a casual bystander but on another baking hot today I am almost like an emergency service. No time for turning any of the pages on that book.

Business is brisk and back breaking. Not exactly like working down the mine, in the shipyard or on a construction site, but still concentrated and cramped. My head scrapes the roof and to talk to a customer I have to bend down and listen carefully. Armed only with a metal scoop, I then have to turn to the side to grab a cone, turn full circle to dip into the churns to grab one or two scoops and place them carefully on the cone. Turning back, with a smile of course and often a merry quip, I hand over the delicacies. Unfortunately, I am not a magician with a quick sleight of hand

and I can only do a couple of ice creams at a time. Then there may be that the chocolate flake to add and the Monkey Blood. Have I mentioned that?

You also have to be patient, treat every customer the same if you can and always be ready for a merry quip or two. It happens to pass the time and keeps the money piling up. The secret is never look bored, no request is too demanding and it really should be service with a smile.

Dog walkers are another set of people worth watching. These are top of the beach user league in my opinion. Bit of bias here as we actually have a family dog. Actually he is a mongrel but that seems to be a bit cruel, more like a bearded collie with other cute bits. He loves the beach but has an irritating habit of occasionally just doing his own thing and wandering off in the opposite direction to you and never showing any hint of returning. Very frustrating to say the least and it does tend to double the time you are out and about. He is probably best described as what you call a 'character'.

Despite this, walking a dog on the beach is one of the great pleasures in life. Beats flying a kite or getting sand out of your sandwich. Generally not too much fuss and not too much bother. Yes, they can make a mess but most of us are responsible and pick it up. And the dogs, along with their owners, come in all shapes and sizes. From little terriers to greyhounds and generally they all seem to get along.

I have to say the sheer sight of your four-legged friend bounding into the waves is sheer delight. Joy unbounded for both you and the dog. Freedom all round. A chance to breathe in life itself. Just the best.

They also make good customers. That is the owners not the dogs. Willing to chat as well as buy. They seem instinctively to know the rules of the outdoors. They always say thanks and they do wag their tails, that is the dogs not the owners. Courteous to a fault. Never demanding and forever grateful.

Others to watch on the beach. There are those messing about in boats. The sailing type, if not the ideal ice cream patrons, are just about acceptable. They are just messing about in the sea. But watching them capsize is always good for a laugh.

On one memorable day the huge rescue helicopter from the nearby RAF base was giving a demonstration just offshore. The wind from the rotor blades was enough to knock several dinghies over. It was like ten pin bowling.

Then we come to speedboats. Don't get me started. Dangerous and in the wrong place. If you want to speed about—go somewhere else, preferably not in a boat. Best in a racing car or on a purpose built circuit miles from other humans and out of reach. Not the open water where others, such as swimmers and small people paddling, have a right to be. You are putting them at risk, never mind the dreadful pollution you are also slipping into the sea. I will put a dinghy on the road. See how you like it when something is clearly in the wrong place.

You are also just showing off. We can see and unfortunately hear just how big and powerful your boat is. Don't really care. Get a fishing rod or a crab line and go on the harbour and see what you can catch. Even better do a bit of rock-pooling or just read a book. Better than catching the irritation and annoyance of just about everyone else.

And why bother trying to tow someone along behind you on with a flimsy rope and on a pair of planks? Nine times out of ten, the attached become quickly detached as they fall headfirst straight into the water on the first thrust. Then you have to start all over again. Tedious to have to watch and probably just as tedious to do. Skiing should be on the Alpine slopes not the northern seas of England.

Context is important here as well. Those with speedboats rarely buy ice cream. By the time they have circled round and round for hours on end, they have probably lost the will to live. I know many of us have. All that money spent on fuel and polluting the waters probably means they can't even afford the smallest cone. They go in the relegation zone as far as beach users are concerned.

Time to mention just one other oddity on the sands. Those with metal detectors. First time I saw someone with one I actually thought they were hoovering the beach. Probably trying to get rid of the sand for the sandwiches. No, they were looking for treasure. They stand for hours, ears plugged in for that sound of something valuable buried deep beneath the sands. They are always on their own. It is a very solitary pastime or occupation, depending just how seriously it is adhered to.

A treasure hunter always seems totally oblivious to the rest of the world. There could be dolphins and seals bobbing up and down in the sea, warships getting ready for battle, cruise liners sweeping by or horses galloping along the beach, and they would never notice. I just hope that there is no one in difficulty near the shore and frantically waving and shouting for help. Heads down and hovering above the sand, they are in a world of their own. It does seem a fairly fruitless task and I just wonder how many hours a day such devotion takes for something that in reality, is never going to happen. But they seem happy and harmless.

Apart from buried beer cans, broken kites and the odd coin, there is probably little else to find. Though with the bloodied history of Northumberland you just never know what might turn up. A Viking helmet, Roman sandal or a monk's habit? That would be good and you do hear of tales of medieval trinkets worth millions being uncovered. I have never seen it happen. I guess the only items buried deep beneath the sands around here may be discarded beer bottles, soft drinks cans, bits of plastic or discarded bottles of Monkey Blood.

Anyway back to work. If I need to build up my own treasure trove I need to sell some ice cream.

1976 And All That

Now, let's get back to basics. As I said before the year is 1976. Records will later show it to be one of the hottest for about three hundred years. I can vouch for that. On one day I was even flagged down by a floundering family by the side of the road. All they wanted was some ice cream, a couple of lollies and some cold canned drinks and they were on their way, suitably resuscitated. I am like an emergency service delivering Red Cross parcels to those in acute risk of overheating in the rapidly rising temperatures and no shelter. I should really have a hose on board and use it as a watery canon to cool people down. Yes, it really is that hot.

Apart from Newcastle's unlucky defeat at Wembley this is also the era for Space Hoppers, Raleigh Choppers and Brotherhood of Man taking Europe by storm with 'Save Your Kisses For Me'. James Callaghan moved into

Number 10 after the resignation of Harold Wilson, Noel Edmunds is thrilling us with Multi Coloured Swap Shop and the police breaking up riots at the Notting Hill Carnival, armed with dustbin lids and milk crates.

Not so happy for the England cricket captain Tony Greig. Before the test series against the West Indies he infamously said: *"I'm not all that worried about them. You must remember that the West Indians, these guys, if they get on top, are magnificent cricketers. But if they're down, they grovel, and I intend to make them grovel."*

Needless to say, they whooped us 3-0 and Greig, who scored just 51 runs in seven innings, got down on his hands and knees and crawled in front of the crowds at the Oval in the final Test.

I am not really a cricket fan but it does make great listening on the radio, a constant companion during these summer months. Much better than having 'Save Your Kisses For Me' blasting out.

What else is happening in 1976? Well records will show that the mercury topped 28C (82F) for 22 days, the Rolling Stones, with a sprightly 33-year-old Mick Jagger, played in front of estimated 200,000 at Knebworth, the average cost of a pint is 32p, petrol 77p a gallon and a loaf of bread about 19p. At the end of August Denis Howell was appointed Minister of Drought and then it started raining.

The Wurzel's infuriatingly keep singing about their combine harvester but at least we have some redemption with the Eagles releasing the classic 'Hotel California' album. The Northumberland coast is a bit like that. *"You can check out but you can never leave."*

In football Lawrie McMenemy's second division underdogs Southampton beat Manchester United 1-0 to win the FA Cup. Why can't Newcastle do that?

There was some North East triumph with Brendan Foster coming back from the Montreal Olympics with a bronze medal after running several laps of the track and the Body

Shop opened its first store in Brighton.

Sylvester Stallone ran up all those steps as the boxer in Rocky and got the best picture Oscar.

It just feels like a good year. Especially round here. The sun just seems to shine without a break and the only clouds I have seen are those with silver linings. One day, when I look back on all this, it will be with a smile.

***

Back to the here and now. How does my day start? The same as any other day. Groundhog Day. Up at about 7.30ish from my slumber in the little caravan that is my home. A quick shower in the nearby block and back for cornflakes and maybe a cuppa. Then it's off.

The caravan site is just behind the Beadnell Hall Hotel, a large palace of a place which in its prime was the hallmark of quality, fine dining and luxury accommodation. More about this later.

My caravan, my summer home, is nestled in a little corner plot with high walls on either side. The neighbouring caravans are all a bit bigger but to be honest, as I am the sole occupant this doesn't really matter. I don't really know the neighbours as they seem to come and go at irregular intervals. I am not really here to be part of this little community as I am here to work. I am away from the site from breakfast time until mid to late evening anyway, so we are like ships that pass in the night.

It is a great base; I can come and go as I please. The caravan is small but perfectly formed. Full cooking facilities, a heater, gas lights and a table that converts into a bed at night. I often come back here after collecting the ice cream van and chatting to colleagues. Nice oasis of calm, coffee and a newspaper, before battle begins. At first I did get strange looks when I had transferred my car for the antiquated mobile retail outlet but fellow caravanners soon got used to the sight. I always make it quite obvious that I am here on a morning break and not set-up for sales. The window remains firmly shut and the Monkey Blood well out of sight. Sometimes it is tempting not to move from here. Leave my van where it is, lie back, read a book and just generally relax. I do admit I occasionally stay here longer than I should before getting back on the road.

I do have one day a week here when I am not working. That really is a day of rest, though I have occasionally nipped back to Newcastle to drop some washing off, repair the balance to my unbalanced diet and generally just a bit of re-fuelling. But at almost a 100-mile round trip it does consume large amounts of time and petrol.

I do occasionally return to my Beadnell caravan later in the day for a few sales but to be honest it is hardly worth as business is never really that good. It also feels odd mixing my office with home. It is best that the two are carefully divided with no blurring of borders. When I am here, I am not at work. To be fair, when I do return in the mid-morning I have never been approached for a sale. My neighbours seem to know the rules and anyhow it is not the time to be tempting would-be customers with quality ices. Most people round here are having a leisurely start to the day, the smell of frying bacon and coffee is still wafting across the land. It is summer, a break from the general trudge of nine to five work, a chance to unwind, no need to rush, soak it all in.

***

Getting in the car and setting off for Seahouses, even though I do it every day, is always a thrill. The drive is barely a couple of miles and the road clings to the sea before entering the hustle and bustle of the tourist hotspot. On the way I pass a large campsite to my left, a large farm, grasslands leading to dunes down to the beach and then the local

Seahouses Golf Club. By the time I arrive, many of the local shops are already open and the first signs of visitors are beginning to surface. This is the time of day I like the best. The calm before the storm, not an ice cream in sight. And who knows what lies ahead. But yet again the skies are an unbroken blue and the temperatures are beginning to rise. The weather is so good you almost expect it. Still there are some people who complain.

"*Don't like it this hot.*"

"*Could do with some rain for the garden.*"

"*It must break sometime. Let's hope so.*"

And some people just can't cope in these soaring temperatures. I see it every day. Bright red bodies stumbling back from the beach as though the sun has caught them by surprise.

"*I only had my shirt off for a few moments. Didn't realise I was beginning to sizzle even though some parts of me were turning redder than usual.*"

"*I wasn't expecting it to be this hot.*"

"*Never really bother with sun lotion. Never*

really need it round here. It is not as though I am in Spain."

There is just something about the weather. It is a topic of conversation every day in this job.

"Weather looks good for another few days."

"Must be good for you. I bet you are selling loads of ice cream."

"You must be busy. Is it not too hot in the van?"

"You picked a fantastic day to be out here."

"Looks like the sunshine is set to last for days. That's what they say, but there again I bet it is raining tomorrow."

"What is a 66 and can I have some Monkey Blood please."

To be fair talking about the weather is a national obsession. We just love talking about it. I read somewhere that we talk about it at least four times a day and this takes up at least eight minutes. We love it. Some experts have us believe it is all down to the fact that the people in this country are generally a reserved bunch.

We don't like to ask people their age or what they do for a living. It is just easier to say *"it was a bit chilly this morning"* or *"I see snow could be on the way soon."*

We are not the only nation. Apparently, the Japanese, who live on a small island, also get excited by sun, rain and wind. Maybe it is because we have such extremities here that there is so much to talk about. We are buffeted by the Atlantic, the North Sea and the Channel, cold winds from the north, the Gulf steam and a myriad or other assorted climatic factors. So you can go out in the sun in your shorts and sandals and come back suffering from hypothermia and frostbite. As they say there is no such thing as bad weather it is just wrong clothing.

We even have own weather-related sayings :

"Saving up for a rainy day."

"Storm in a teacup."

"I am feeling under the weather."

"It's brass monkeys out there."

"Phew what a scorcher."

Doesn't really bother me. I will talk to anybody about anything as long as it's not too deep, intellectual or controversial. One thing I have learned very quickly is to keep words short and simple and just keep turning round, crouching down and scooping out the scoops for one and all. I don't think I have really ever had an argument with anybody even though my patience has been stretched on more than one occasion. It gets a bit frantic when you have a large queue and a family in front who have no idea what they want.

"Now let's see. What have we got here? Ice creams, lollies, drinks. What does anybody want? Come here, let's have a look and see what there is."

"Right, an ice cream, an orange lolly, a wafer, a 99, a 66. What is a 66 by the way? An upside down 99?"

"No, right, you don't want a wafer. You want a 99. How about the rest of us? Are you sure

you just want a drink. Can't tempt you with a chocolate flake and a cone. No, okay, an ice cream or a drink. No you can't have both. It is one or the other."

"Come on. The poor man is waiting to hear what you want. Here we go, two 99's, no make that three, a nougat wafer and a couple of lollies please. No sorry, make that three lollies and just a 66 rather than a 99. No hang about, a 99, much bigger. That's all thanks."

"Right, how much is that? What, how much? Now wait a minute I think I have left my wallet on the beach. Oh no, here it is, in my back pocket. I will just see how much I have got. You must be making a fortune today. Bet you wish there were more people like me around. You could retire at these prices. Never mind, we are all here on holiday..."

"There you go. Oh sorry. I forgot to ask. Can I have a bit of Monkey Blood on the 66, sorry 99, and I have forgotten someone. No, I have forgotten two. Can you give me a couple more 99's as well?"

"Oh hi there. Haven't seen you for a while. Up to much today? I am just getting some ice creams. Fancy one? Yes, great. A 99? No, a 66 then? That's just an upside down 99. Go on then, another 66 for my mate here. And I think that's it."

About time too. Most of those in the queue have lost the will to live. I know the feeling. They have decided not to wait. Can't really blame them. This shipping order has taken well over ten minutes. An awful long time if you are the unlucky person just standing behind. I manage to maintain a smile throughout the whole transaction and just keep going.

I have the odd occasion when an ice cream has been dropped in handover. Not a good sight for anyone and a bit damaging for the old reputation. The fallen object, lying in an unsightly mess on the ground, is always replaced by a free replica as I quickly move on.

"Next please."

"Two 99's and a nougat wafer please. Thought I would never get served. Only joking. Not your fault. Everyone seems to want an ice cream today. Fantastic weather, bet you are glad you came here out today. Might be rain tomorrow. The gardens certainly need it."

For some people this is paradise. Queuing and talking about the weather. Just how thoroughly more British can you get. Our two favourite pastimes at once. It always amazes me that some people think waiting in a queue is all part of the fun. The true British holiday experience.

If we see a queue we just have to join it. There must be something interesting happening. Possibly it all goes back to rationing during the war when people had to wait in line for food, or maybe it just gives us a bit more time to talk about the weather.

The history of the British queue is said to date back to the Industrial Revolution, which saw huge numbers of people working in factories where everyone started and finished at the same time, creating crowds waiting to punch in their timecards or grab groceries after clocking out.

But now it is just a way of life. We love it so much that we often tend to join a queue and then ask what it's for.

For me this is hard work. Constantly turning round, bending down and being nice. But the wooden tray is already filling up nicely with lots of notes and coins. It is a good day.

This stretch of coast is just a tiny part of Northumberland. It is a huge county and the last bit of land that separates England from Scotland. It has been fought over for centuries and you almost smell the taste of battle; every inch hides a piece of history and heritage.

Romans, Vikings, Anglo Saxon kings, monks and the vicious fighting gangs of the Border Reivers have all left their mark. Violence and conflict everywhere.

That legacy can still be seen today as the land has more castles than any other county. You are barely yards away from one fortress or another at any given moment—some in ruins, others lived in and all still standing in some shape or other, some have seen better days and others that would be classed, in estate agent jargon, as *"desirable residences with a little bit updating needed."*

When the Romans came here some 2000 years ago they decided to build a wall to guard the wild northern frontier of their ever expanding empire. Now there's a job you wouldn't want. No cement, no bricks, no short cuts.

You can imagine the guys saying to Emperor Hadrian...

"Yeah we can build you a wall governor. You say 73 miles long, the odd fort here, some living quarters, baths and bakeries. Should take two to three months. No problem. Will drop you a quote. "

Some six years later and it was finally completed. Only bits of it are left now, but every year the odd Roman sandal or bit of a helmet is still being uncovered. Time to get those treasure detectors out.

Apart from hauling large stones up hills and across moors to put the whole thing together, the other job not to apply for would have been a Roman guard. Roaming the wall, maybe that is where the name Romans came from, in uncomfortable armour and open-toed sandals, in biting winds and darkness, would not exactly be living the dream. Still someone had to do it I suppose. There would certainly be a cold wind up most parts.

Northumberland is a wonderful mix of rolling moorland, hills and coast. Most people live in the industrial south east where coal is still just about king and the rest sprawls out to where there are more sheep than humans.

Here, on this gloriously sunny day, there are definitely more humans than sheep around the coast. Good thing too. I have never seen a sheep queue for a cornet yet. They are just happy with grass.

***

It is all peace and tranquillity at the moment. Here at Beadnell harbour I am just waiting for my first sale of the day and there is plenty of time for my mind to wander. Hard to think that just up the road near the border there was once an almighty skirmish between England and Scotland at the infamous Battle of Flodden. It was bigger than anything at Wembley or Hampden Park.

They were thousands slaughtered, including the Scottish captain, King James IV, as his army was savagely beaten by the enemy. It all happened in September 1513.

How many Scottish lives were lost at Flodden conflict are unknown, but it is thought to be between 10,000 to 17,000 men. Despite initial Scottish success, the battle was a devastating defeat for the Scots. Casualties were very heavy and amongst all those killed were nine earls, thirteen barons, five heirs to titles, three bishops, two abbots, along with the King himself. The English fatalities totaled somewhere around 1,500.

The Scottish army was armed with French long pikes, a useful weapon against cavalry but useless in close combat. Most died in the shallow dip known as the Killing Field—then an area of marshland. The thick mud of the marshes created poor footing, where the long pikes used by the Scots were impossible to wield. In just a few hours some 14,000 men lay dead or dying on the Killing Fields, a worse rate of slaughter than the WWI Battle of the Somme.

The site is well worth a visit as you soon get a sense of the true carnage and almost hear the battle and touch the ghosts of combat. All part of the bloody history of Northumberland.

Across to the west of the county are the Cheviot Hills, a barren but accessible range of climbs, where getting to the top can be rewarded with glorious views, although there are many peat bogs to clamber across and lose your wellies.

Yes, Northumberland is a vast and varied

county, rich in history and heritage and some of the best scenery around. But to be honest, my favourite spots are on the coast. I do like to be by the seaside. I am just lucky to be here by the seaside. I do like it here.

The commute to work is barely two miles from Beadnell to Seahouses. I could walk or run there but no time for that or even the inclination. Why would you? Fortunately I have the luxury of a car. A lovely maroon, Morris Minor estate—a classic. Even though it also has flip out indicators, it is more reliable than the old van I spend most of days in.

I am in Seahouses in about five minutes and meet up with the rest of the gang. A varied bunch I can tell you. There is another student, in it for the short term and two elder gentlemen. Kings of the road as I like to call them; they have been doing this job for years. They are local, wise and caring. My mentors. There is also a guy I rarely see, he seems fairly old, has really thick glasses and is hauled off to the harbour at Seahouses every morning in one of the static set-ups. I don't think I have ever met him. Doesn't really seem to part of the team. But that is absolutely fine.

My student friend seems to have a busy life outside ice cream and out of office. He has long hair, big sideburns and often arrives at work with large bruises on his neck. Being innocent and naive I just thought he must have that type of skin which seems to turn the darkest shade of blue at the slightest touch. Maybe he is just prone to falling over a lot or maybe accidentally stabbed himself with a sharp cornet. He is also obsessed with cameras, some kind of would-be photographer I think, but I never delve too deep.

Then the penny dropped when I saw him driving around one night with a young lady at his side and 'Shooting Star' by Bad Company blasting out of every window.

'Well Johnny was a schoolboy when he heard his first Beatles song

Love Me Do I think it was and from there it

didn't take him long'

And then ends rather sadly...

'Well Johnny died one night, died in his sleep

A bottle of whisky, sleeping tablets by his bed

Johnny's life passed him by like a warm summer's day

If you listen to the wind you can still hear him play'

I think my temporary colleague sees him himself as a bit of rock star and those marks on his neck are just from wild abandonment and liaison from the night before. Wild women and wild nights. Maybe it is just an image and nothing else. Still, he is always fun to have around.

By the time I arrive, the fleet of vans, well about four of them, are already being given manicures in the yard where they are stored. Not mine as I am last on the scene as usual. There is no real rush to get started. Most people around here are having a leisurely breakfast. You can still smell the bacon wafting in the air. An ice cream is not on the menu just yet. I love the smell of frying in the morning. It mixes well with the sea air and the seagulls.

Our ice cream fleet also includes a couple of static units, as already indicated, which have to be towed into place by the boss's Land Rover every morning. One goes down to the harbour in Seahouses and another goes to a car park in Bamburgh.

I always think being assigned to one of those would be too shackling. Nowhere to go. Stuck in one place all day. No chance of skiving off to some remote spot where no one can see you, have a nap, read a book or go for a walk—and you have set start and finishing times. Like a glider, you take off when the tow line is dropped and then the day ends when you are dragged back to the hangar, or in this case, the back yard.

They always remind me of some kind of

prison van. The guys inside are shackled to their duties, no say in where they go or when they come back. They have lost their freedom, their rights to roam and may as well be handcuffed. Not for me. No, I prefer the open road. Born to be wild and born to run and all that.

To coin a phrase or a good lyric:

'Get your motor runnin', looking for adventure, and whatever comes our way running, like a true nature's child, we can climb so high, I never wanna to die.

Born to be wild.

Born to be wild'

I signed up for travel. Not sure what would have happened if I turned up on the first day and was told I would be stuck in one place all summer. Probably just hunched my shoulders, gone in the huff and said: *"Ok, you are the boss."* I am not one for conflict, but I have to say it would have been a pretty long and fairly boring assignment to say the least. Same place, same view and probably the same people every day. No thanks.

Anyhow, no need to dwell on that. My van is here and waiting. Another day of adventure.

We always start off with a brew and a chat. It is all very friendly and undemanding. Just general chit chat over a cup of coffee. Although we are all different in age, outlook and experience, we do feel like brothers in arms, all with a common aim, camaraderie and chirpiness. I really do enjoy the company, the gossip, the tales and the sense of humour. It is all innocent and convivial. But even though I am from just fifty miles down the road at Newcastle, the language is completely different up here.

The Geordie accent surrounding the banks of the Tyne is well known and often imitated. But head a bit further north up to this part of world and you stumble on the Northumbrian burr.

It is a throaty guttural sound that surfaces

around the letter R. It really does seem to come from well down in the dungeons of the body and concludes with a lovely gentle rolling sound. Maybe quite hard to explain if you have never come across it. You really have to hear it to get the full affect.

Everywhere else I am called Ron because that is my name. No complications, easy to spell, easy to pronounce and little options for variations...

Not in Seahouses and surrounding areas. The R at the start of the name is rolled out and Ron become 'Rern' or sometimes 'Rernie'. Go on have a go at saying it. Just for fun you can always ask a Northumbrian to recant *'Around the ragged rock the ragged rascal ran'* and then you will get the full impact. It is a wonderful and unique dialect.

The throaty sound is known as a BURR but is sometimes referred to as a WHARLE. Who knows the derivation, there are many tales into how it all started, some tall and others even taller. One that stretches the imagination is the dubious claim it came from people copying a speech defect of Sir Henry Percy, a son of the Earl of Northumberland, in the 1300s. But as we know, Northumberland is a county with a long and involved history with many influences, ranging from the Vikings to the Scots, so maybe a cocktail of these is a more probable explanation.

I love it. It is like a warm blanket. Very comfortable. I could listen to it all day long and I really enjoy our morning chats with the team, especially when they have to say Ron and ice cream in the same sentence. But I do feel really welcome, valued and trusted, which is comforting in itself. I like being called Rern or Rernie. Makes it feel as though I have been accepted. One of the tribe. One of the gang. One for all and all for one.

The morning talk over a cup of coffee is always the same but still good to be a part of. *How was yesterday? Did you sell much?* This is normally aimed at Frank, not his real name but I would like to spare his blushes. He has a set circuit every day. He is a local man and his community depend on him for essential deliveries. He spends every working day meandering around the many little hamlets and houses where he is recognised just as much as the local postman. He lives here, he has responsibilities, a sense of belonging. He is incredibly well organised, neat and tidy. His van is spotless and everything is lined up in a uniform and precise arrangement. Unlike me and thousands of others who will soon have to return to our sterile urban lives, Frank remains a resident and no doubt a pillar of the community, all year round. I really like him. He does tend to be a bit serious about what he does but that is totally fine.

His routine answer to our routine questioning about his previous day sales is always the same. "*Not much ice cream but you bugger I sold some pop.*" You see he likes to be well stocked on a range of bottled drinks.

For Frank these are his banker. It is his reliable seller no matter what the weather.

Come rain or shine he will always sell some pop. In contrast, for me it is an unnecessary and unwelcome addition. The bottles stack up and make the van even more crammed than usual. I tend to stock as few as possible. I do have a few cans of soft drinks—these are smaller, easily stored and can be good sellers. I have one or two myself everyday but don't tell the boss or the doctor.

I wouldn't dare go into the villages where Frank goes. I know the rules, the pecking order and there are some things you just don't do. I respect Frank. He is from here, one of the community he so loyally serves and is just a top bloke. Fairly quiet but never a cross word about anybody. In the same way he never ventures down to Beadnell harbour. He knows this is my territory and he is happy with that.

The other regular guy is Jimmy, often referred to as Mr Bamburgh or The Conefather. The elder statesman of our group. I will tell you more about him as my summer continues. He is quiet, polite and one I feel I need to look up to for guidance. His van is always spotless, his white coat pristine and his manners impeccable. I imagine his ice cream comes with five star silver service. He is quality personified. Takes a huge pride in his job. Nothing is ever out of place. I have visions that during the lean winter months he is a butler in some stately home.

My boss always seems to be here in the morning. Never far away. Always checking everything is alright. Making sure I had a good day yesterday and set for another good day today. He provides the float, the loose change, quickly inspects my van and is generally there to keep on top of everything, making sure standards don't slip. He is paying my wages and my welfare is his welfare. We get on well and I know as long as you do the work, you will be fairly rewarded. He doesn't always have a great deal to say but that is the way it should be and is very much the silent type. Not quite the silent assassin but somebody you probably don't want to cross. He just likes to keep an eye on things. It is his business and the season is short and there should be some distance between the guy in charge and his workers. Wouldn't be good to get too friendly.

Right, we have had our chat, had a coffee and examined the retail value of assorted drinks in bottles. Now it is time make sure my van has been cleaned properly, spick as span as possible, but never as spick or span as the others in the fleet. Occasionally this does require a quick hosing all the way round the outside. Nice to have a gleaming vehicle. Tends to let people think you are reliable, hygienic and healthy.

Sort of: *"Yes, I would certainly buy and ice cream from that van. If it looks that good then the ice cream must be good."*

Unfortunately my van doesn't really fall into that category. As already mentioned it would be more at home at a vintage vehicle rally, fitting in neatly alongside steam engines and men with handlebar moustaches in tweed waistcoats and flat caps. In a funny kind of way it could be the novelty look that gets them queuing.

"Look at that. It must be a hundred years old. Can't believe what I am seeing. Must go and have a look and see what it is selling. Come and join me everybody."

It is the interior that is really important. Now that has to be clean. Don't really want to be closed down for flouting any hygiene rules or falling foul of health and safety standards. That would be a waste of this hottest of all hot summers.

So after a good scrub down it is time for stocking up. In go a couple of crates of those pop bottles. Just for appearance really. I have no intention of selling any. There is not much money to be made there. Then there a few cans of well-known soft drinks. They can sell reasonably well even though there is nowhere cold to store them. Next come the lollies. Orange, chocolate, rocket shaped, lemonade, oblong, round, square. I pile them in.

Cones next. I go for simplicity. Single cones only. And they are all the same. Don't give people more choice than there already is. The life of an ice cream man is complicated enough.

Then there are the boxes, chocolate flakes and some wafers. More about wafers later.

Here we go. The real ammunition. Climb the few steps that lead to the epicentre of it all. The ice cream making factory. Okay, I exaggerate again. We are in Seahouses after all, not the heart of Italy where ice cream is a way of life. No, the factory is, in essence just a little room above the Milk Bar.

Imagine a roundabout with a fish and chip shop and gift shop on one side and the Milk Bar on the other. The secret room where the white stuff is made is on that other side, above the Milk Bar.

The Milk Bar is a great little place, run by the same people who run this ice cream business. Not really sure it actually sells milk but does offer a range of coffees, teas, sandwiches and the ice cream we sell.

Always think selling ice cream from here is a neat touch. It is like a little taster which hopefully will leave people wanting more.

"See that van at the harbour. It sells the same ice cream as that Milk Bar in Seahouses. It is really good. I can recommend it. In fact I may get myself another one. I am told they have 66's and Monkey Blood. Come on. Follow me."

The ice cream factory is only accessed by a set of wooden steps leading to a wooden door and once inside you soon realise it is barely big enough to swing a 99 in never mind an ice cream scoop, cat or anything else. And it is a secret chamber. I am not joking. Jonny, again not his real name in fear of defamation, is in charge. It is his domain. He will take the recipe to his grave. I have no idea how he makes it. All I know he makes plenty of it and it is up to us to get out there and sell it.

As we are by the sea I am informed that the term 'swing a cat' originates from old sailing vessels, where the phrase refers to a space too small to easily swing a cat of nine tails, a kind of whip used for physical punishment aboard ship.

The ice cream in my van is stored in milk churns and I can fit two or three in the fridge at a time. Some days I have to come back for more. A bit like a modern day Oliver Twist. Once Jonny knows you are a competent ice cream man you can consider yourself one of the family. He is our Fagan.

He is also very jolly. A man happy at his work. Pay as you churn. He always has a hearty greeting and is especially jovial at the moment as his makes ice cream while the sun seems to be constantly shining. The more he has to make the happier he seems to be. He has the recipe for success. I really have no idea what time he starts work. I suspect it is under cover of darkness and he is escorted to his little factory by security guards in sunglasses for fear of ambush and being forced to reveal the whole ice cream making process.

We can talk about everything but the recipe. As long as I am collecting the churns as fast as he is churning them out, then everyone is happy. We always shoot the breeze with merry quips, lots of laughter and a serious sense of fun in the sun. He is the main man, the centre of it all, but he bears the weighty responsibility with lightweight shoulders. Only one complaint. He never helps you up and down the wooden steps with the churns. No, his job is making the ice cream and filling them up. You have to do the rest. I have often been tempted to roll the churns down the steps towards my van like some kind of seaside ten pin bowling. But then this quickly disappears along with the image of a churn tumbling past the van, across the roundabout and demolishing the carefully arranged buckets, spades and beach balls outside the gift shop. It is still tempting. Might do it on my last day. Go out with a bang.

The vans all queue up neatly outside the

Milk Bar like a squadron for Spitfires waiting for take-off or invading tanks ready to roll into enemy territory. Fortunately the only ammunition is ice cream, Monkey Blood and chocolate flakes but enough to leave the trenches, fearlessly face the frontline and capture a few customers.

At times we do feel like an army, a band of brothers, boldly going into battle. The meticulous planning, the routes all mapped out and we all know what we are doing and where we have to go. This is it. No going back now. Let's get out there.

All I know about ice cream, especially the stuff that we sell, is the fact it is absolutely delicious. I should know I have eaten enough myself. Probably eating into the profits at the same time. It is quality ice cream. Once tasted I can guarantee you will come back for more. Well, that's my theory and it certainly seems to be the recipe for success in these parts.

As for that recipe. I know it involves a lot of milk. Probably a bit of sugar and maybe a few eggs. We only sell one flavour. Vanilla. The real deal. None of this strawberry or raspberry ripple nonsense. This is Seahouses. Nothing fancy around here.

Flavouring? If you want you can add a chocolate flake or two and a bit of Monkey Blood. Oh no, there it is again. I do and try and blur it from my mind. I sometimes forget to refill the bottle. But if there is none left my customers would be revolting.

Once the churns are in place I am like that Spitfire or tank and ready to roll into action. Beadnell harbour here I go. I never bore of the scenery. Another day in the frontline, Beadnell or bust. You have to pick a pocket or two.

***

When I take an order I literally have to scoop the ice cream out of the churn in the cool compartment and onto the cone. It is really basic. None of this pressing a button and it all comes squirting out nonsense. I am doing it the way it has probably been done for years. Why change a winning formula?

I am supposed to wear a pristine white jacket every day. It does look good when it is clean, but that is a rarity. How Jimmy gets his coat so white is a mystery. I guess he must have a complete wardrobe and is able to wear a new one every day. More often than not, mine is covered in that much Monkey Blood and assorted residue from flavoured lollies, that I either look like a hippy in some way-out floral attire or someone who has been routinely beaten up by a rival gang. I have to confess I have taken to hanging it in the van, just in view of the boss but not too close for inspection. This gives the impression that I will be putting on the kit as soon as I hit the road.

My uniform is jeans, trainers and T-shirt with the added addition of a jumper or sweatshirt if the temperatures dip. I occasionally wear sunglasses to look slightly cooler and mysterious. Not sure if they do project such an image but I would like to think so, especially if there is a bit of Beach Boys blasting out on the radio. Always good to look the part.

After the morning conference I am on my way. Supplied, stocked and set-up for the day. My routine is fairly regular and once again I am off to the harbour at Beadnell. I know it well, it is safe, secure and a great selling spot. With the beach in front of me, the lime kilns nearby and the cobles bobbing up and down, it is just a perfect spot. Cobles are a traditional fishing boat, flat bottomed, open and more akin to a large rowing boat than an ocean going vessel. But they seem to do the job as the fishermen return with assorted lobsters and crabs and catch the attention of early morning tourists and seagulls alike. These men are a hardy and hardworking bunch and it is great to chat to them. They certainly have a wonderful Burr about them, lyrical and mesmerising.

I don't really mind sitting here all day and not selling a thing. Well, not really; for I start I would probably be sacked, then there is the case of not making any money. I am paid a set wage, just under £30 for a six-day week. Before you think I must be a mug, I am also on commission and get ten pence from every pound I make. It all adds up to a tidy sum and it is great work as I simply love being beside the seaside. Watching the tide going in out, the salty smell, seaweed and seagulls are enough for me. It is my own paradise. Well, maybe not my own, but I don't mind sharing it, especially when I have ice cream to sell and money to be made.

And I do feel important. Probably a completely ridiculous thing to say. But I do have the feeling I would be missed if I wasn't around. I am not saying that in some kind of arrogant or alarming way. If not me, then the fantastic ice cream itself would be missed. Ice cream and the seaside go together like bread and butter, buckets and spades, seagulls and squawking.

My van is as integral to coastal picture as

the sand dunes, the harbour, the sea and the seagulls. I would like to think my ice cream van would be a part of any artist trying to sketch and reproduce the very fabric of Beadnell and surrounding areas. A harbour has to have boats and this harbour needs an ice cream van.

I may have missed a trick here. I could and should have made some postcards with my mobile retail cold confectionery outlet heavily featured. I am sure they would be a popular companion to the ever faithful Puffins on tea towels. I could display the postcards in the window, alongside the Monkey Blood and cans of drink. They could be my little added extra income on the side. I may have to patent this idea.

The Faraway Farnes

They are about the most popular visitors around here.

They are unmistakable. Once seem, never forgotten. Complete with a funny walk and a loud mouth, they stumble around in large groups.

Not the ones who have had too much sun and too much beer and can be seen staggering around at night. To see what I am talking about you have to make a real effort.

One more clue. They are often seen on tea towels. Bit of a giveaway there. Yes they are Puffins. Up there at the top of the perch as far as favourite birds go. Because of their vivid marking and bright orange bills they are known as sea parrots. You can see why.

You have to hop on a boat and nip across to the Farne Islands to get up close and personal with them. You can easily see the islands from the shore at Seahouses and beyond as they rise above the sea like a small fleet of battle grey warships.

Today as usual there are large queues outside the wooden huts that line up against the sea wall down to the main harbour at Seahouses offering trips to the islands. There is a queue so we have to join it to see what all the fuss is about. I can see the islands as I load the van. I have been across to them and it is a good day out. You can get on a boat to sail round the islands and return without setting foot on soil or go for the better deal with trips that to land on the islands and give you the opportunity to walk round for about an hour or so.

Apart from the sea parrots there are also hundreds of other birds of the sea to spot. All sorts of gulls, Arctic Terns, the dubiously named Shags along with Kittiwakes, Razorbills, Eider Ducks and Guillemots.

Getting on board one of the many day-tripper boats is an experience in itself. For a start they offer hardly any shelter from any storms. They are completely open to the elements. Apart from the driver that is, perhaps best referred to as the skipper, who has a little cabin all to himself. Even the one or two deckhands, there to help you on and off and untie and tie the ropes, are as uncovered as the rest of the passengers.

First of all is the perilous descent of steep steps to actually get on the boats right at the very outpost of the harbour. Getting down these is an achievement in itself and the waiting crews at the bottom always seem to look on with a sense of both amusement and trepidation. There are the odd occasions when severe winds and choppy waters lead to cancellations. But these tend to be few and far between, as those taking us to the Farne Islands and those going are a hardy lot. A gust of wind and a few waves are not going to put them off.

The passengers are normally a motley crew, a mixed bag of human kind. They range from those clad head to toe, in essential wildlife watching gear, to excited youngsters in flip-flops and sun hats. The first group, the real enthusiasts, who no doubt subscribe to National Geographic Magazine and pretend they do this all the time, come complete with sturdy boots, waterproofs, fleeces, bobble hats, gloves, maps and backpacks big enough for a large fridge and maybe the kitchen sink. They are always the same, no matter if it is raining or sunny. They are highly competitive. Who has the biggest and best equipment? Cameras, binoculars and telescopes of all shapes and sizes—some with lenses almost as long as the boat. These can probably pinpoint life on Mars or pick out what Neil and Buzz left behind on their sojourn to the moon.

There is constant chatter, the experts with notebooks and the families with excited youngsters. There is space for everyone.

The excitement tends to rise as the boat gets nearer the islands. The first sight of a seal is greeted with lots of finger pointing, clicking and shrieks of delight. What is more worrying is the group dash to one side for a better view, promptly followed by a dash back to the other side as more seals appear. It feels the whole vessel might just tip over as it rocks from side to side in alarming fashion. None of this bothers the seals one jot. They rarely look flustered and just seem a bit bored with the constant stream of day-trippers gawping at them but always happy to oblige.

"*Okay, take another picture if you want.*"

"*Wait a minute, do you want us to smile and wave? No problem.*"

"*That's it. I'm off back to the rocks for a bit of a rest. See you next time.*"

There is lot of history attached to these rocky outcrops. Benedictine monks, a quiet bunch by all accounts, lived here and there are still the odd ruins of ancient chapels.

Nowadays the only human occupants are volunteers who sporadically inhabit the islands to count the numbers of seals. Not quite sure how they do that as they all tend to look the same, that is the seals not the volunteers. Come to think of the volunteers do all look fairly similar. Floppy waterproof hats, threadbare fleeces, solid walking boots and carrying notebooks and binoculars.

They must have regular recounts before the final results. Well, it passes the time when there is nothing else to do. Not as though you can nip down the pub for a quick pint and grab fish and chips on the way home. Counting seals is probably a good way of getting to sleep.

Being a volunteer does sound kind of idyllic though. Cut off from everyday modern life. Peace and tranquillity. Maybe, they are some kind of modern monks.

And every year, almost without fail, our happy band of seal counters are besieged by television crews falling over themselves to tell the story of their unique lifestyle and how they survive. It is the same script every time.

"Yes, we are here for several weeks. No one else around. Cook and look after ourselves. Count the seals, check on the Puffins and then

the next day check on the Puffins and count the seals."

Still, it seems to make popular viewing but I always have the nagging thought that after the cameras are gone, the real action begins. Puffins against volunteers in a game of football with the seals refereeing and then all sharing a few pints afterwards. Maybe I have been on my own too long.

The Farne Islands are home to thousands of grey seals, also known as Atlantic seals, and each autumn hundreds of pups are born here.

More seal facts for you. The males have a lifespan of between 20 to 25 years with the females living a bit longer to about 30 to 35 years. The grey seals spend about 80% of their time underwater and only come up for air. They stay submerged for up to eight minutes at a time and get reach depths of around 30 metres.

And those monks living on these islands

were a greedy bunch as they actually harvested the seals. They were valued because of the oil that could be extracted from their carcasses and also as a luxury food. As creatures of the sea, seals counted as fish and could be eaten on a Friday. Not so sure you get seal and chips in Seahouses today, cod and haddock tend to the favourites.

There are thousands of pairs of Puffins on the Farnes as they come here to breed every year between April and July, with May and June being peak breeding season. For the rest of the year, they fly out to sea. While on the water they shed their brightly coloured bills for a dull grey version. The vibrant colours somehow return when spring comes around, but I think they may have secretly stored away false orange noses and just put them on for the tourists, tea towel manufactures and photographers.

But getting off the boat to wander around

the wildlife is certainly well worth it. Always a thrill. But beware of those birds flying low like the Dambusters and pecking unprotected heads. They seem to think it is fun.

I was on a boat one day and I noticed some passengers wearing tin like helmets. At first I thought they may be from a D-Day re-enactment group, but when we landed they certainly had the last laugh. The headwear proved just the job to stop the birds treating your scalp as a tasty snack. It is a great day out. Refreshing, exhilarating and a reminder just what good old fashioned sea air can do for the soul, uplifting and those fish and chips always taste better when you get your land legs back.

Never mind the Puffins what about the famous sea rescue that took place just off the Farne Islands I hear you ask? I was coming to that. Rich in folklore and rich in drama.

It all centres around a 22-year-old woman called Grace. Now she must have had a hard life. The seventh of nine children, four brothers and four sisters, she helped look after the Longstone lighthouse and cottage on the islands where her father was the keeper. It was back in the Victorian days. As a maid, not only did she wash, cook, clean, it also seems she was in charge of the family rowing boat.

One stormy night, September 1838, she happened to look out the window and in thick fog and gale force winds she noticed a boat floundering against the rocks. It was the steamship Forfarshire making its way from Hull to Dundee. Not entirely sure why. Possibly an early equivalent of a modern day cruise liner. Anyhow there were at least 60 people on board.

Her Dad must have noticed it as well. He shouted up something along the lines... *"Grace, darling, sorry to be a nuisance but I have just spotted a boat that seems to been sliding towards us. Could you make me a quick cup of tea and then if you have a moment maybe get our boat out and nip across and see what it going on."*

Possibly not factually correct. Her name actually was Grace Darling and she did later receive £50 from the then 19-year-old Queen Victoria for her valiant efforts.

They rowed across raging seas to the Harcar Rock. Here, William went ashore leaving Grace to keep the boat in position. Rowing against the tide and gales they took five survivors back to the lighthouse from the grounded wreck. William, with the help of others, returned later to help pick up others. It is believed more than 40 lives had been lost.

The Times newspaper asked the question: "*Is there in the whole field of history, or of fiction even, one instance of female heroism to compare for one moment with this?*" Answers on a postcard please.

Apart from Royal recognition, Grace was also besieged by people coming to the islands just to get a glimpse of her and she was also inundated for locks of her hair. It is said such unwanted stardom all got a bit much and tragically she died barely two years later.

It is an inspirational tale and yet another reason why a visit to this wonderful part of the world should be on everyone's bucket-list. Not the list that includes spades of course, but please don't tell too many people about the miles of deserted golden sands, the castles, the history, the Puffins or the ice cream. We want you to visit. Just not in huge numbers. It is just nice as it is.

From The Bronx To Bamburgh

As you may have gathered this part of the world is not exactly the Bronx, inner city London or the infamous Gorbals in Glasgow. What skirmishes there have been around here are in the distant past. Rampaging Scots trying to take over the land, Romans building barricades, the Border Reivers fighting everybody. Bit of a bloody history. Even Berwick, just up the road, is supposedly still at war with Russia after a peace treaty was never signed. The town, the most northerly in England, still can't make up its mind where it should be. The football team, Berwick Rangers, play in the Scottish league.

Their great claim to fame which is still talked about to this day came in 1967 when the second division club, complete with part-timers, beat the mighty Glasgow Rangers 1-0, a team packed with in internationals, in one of the greatest Scottish Cup upsets ever.

Nearly 14,000 were crammed into Shielfield Park that day and everyone in Berwick mysteriously still claim they were there. Jock Wallace, the home goalkeeper, rubbed salt into the wound by saying he played the entire second half with only one contact lens after losing the other in the mud.

***

My own upset came this gloriously sunny day on the Northumberland coast. It was only afterwards that I realised there was another ice cream business in town. Hard to believe in such a small place. The one I work for is naturally considered the best, the most popular and the most widely recognised. When you see our distinctive blue and cream coloured fleet you know it means quality.

I didn't know we had competition. I had noticed a couple of other vans but thought they were just passing through. I later realised they were actually based in Seahouses. It took a long time for the penny to drop as I had never given them a second thought and had never seen them stop and sell anything.

All that changed this particular day, quicker than I could say "*Do you want Monkey Blood with that?*" With the sun still shining I decide to go off-piste for a change, slide out of my comfort zone and get a change of scenery. The road out of Seahouses to Bamburgh is short but scenic. There are wonderful views of that stunning castle, and the beach is hidden behind a string of grassed areas behind the dunes.

I had never really looked at these as potential selling hotspots. Bit of a schoolboy error as they are often pretty packed with those beach nomads setting off for another day on the sand and in the sea. Bit of a captive audience really. Today was no exception. The bucket, spades and windshield gangs were all there. I could catch them as they headed towards the sands or were ambling their way back.

Let's go for it. Mirror, signal, maneuver, and I am in place. The van is now nicely tucked in just behind a row of cars and near the sandy path through the dunes to the beach. Bingo. This looks good. There are vehicles parked everywhere and in no particular order. A bit like pebbles scattered across the landscape. No formality, no neat rows, no allocated parking spaces, and no charges. I suppose when it's free parking you just leave your vehicle wherever you want. All a bit haphazard but I don't care. Boots are already open, kids running around excitedly as already frazzled adults look on and try and lift assortment seaside equipment single-handed. But it all looks innocent and carefree. There is a tangible sense of excitement.

Switch off the engine, up and out of my seat and up and at them. I have barely slid the window back and a queue is already forming. Why didn't I think of coming here before? It is such an obvious choice. Sometimes you can miss an open goal. I have driven past so many times without ever venturing in. No logic really. Sometimes the blindingly obvious can be just that. You don't see it.

All looking good as I serve my first customers. I have never been this busy so quickly. This is the way to make money and fast. Maybe I will give Beadnell a miss in the future and just come straight here. Mind you I can't see the sea or the beach, just a tantalising glimpse from of the back of the dunes. Feels like I am behind the scenes rather than on stage. Still, if business is as brisk this every day, well who needs a room with a view when you can cash in like this? *'Art for art's sake, money for God's sake'* to coin another well-known lyric.

I am a bit obsessed with songs as you can see. I do blame Mr Dylan. Ever since I swapped my copy of 'Deep Purple in Rock' for Bob Dylan's Greatest Hits with a fellow pupil at school, I was hooked. Strangely the double album, inside a neat folding blue cover, weren't even his greatest hits. Just another way of teasing us. But later, as I heard even more of his songs, I realised that anyone who can come up with *'the ghost of electricity howls in the bones of her face'* just has to be a creative genius. The greatest wordsmith since Shakespeare. I could go on for hours and often do. How about *'I was so much older then but I am younger than that now'* or *'you don't need a weatherman to know which way the wind blows.'* Classic and timeless.

And of course, he is Mr Tambourine Man himself.

'And take me disappearing through the smoke rings of my mind
Down the foggy ruins of time
Far past the frozen leaves
The haunted frightened trees
Out to the windy beach
Far from the twisted reach of crazy sorrow
Yes, to dance beneath the diamond sky
With one hand waving free

Silhouetted by the sea

Circled by the circus sands

With all memory and fate

Driven deep beneath the waves

Let me forget about today until tomorrow'

Hey, Mr. Tambourine Man, play a song for me

I'm not sleepy and there is no place I'm going to

Hey, Mr. Tambourine Man, play a song for me

In the jingle jangle morning, I'll come following you'

See what I mean. One day he will be truly rewarded for his clever words and his significant contribution to literature.

He was once asked what his songs were about, and he replied along the lines... 'S*ome are about two minutes or three minutes, and some are even longer.'* Wit as well as wisdom.

Anyhow, times were about to change here and the blowing in the wind ready to turn direction and brew up a storm. The good is about to turn bad and ugly. Here I am in this bonanza of a beauty spot just off the road between Seahouses and Bamburgh, where I feel I may have just cracked a safe. The banter begins. It is all very innocent, and the routine script is a routine as always.

"Great day for the beach,"

"Yes, we are really looking forward it. And the sun is shining again. You have got a great spot here."

"What can I get you?"

"Not sure. I fancy a 66, what is that? An upside down 99? And what do you want kids? Four ordinary cones, an orange lolly and a couple of your cans of pop please. Doesn't matter if they are not cold."

"Great. Just give me a second. Have you come far? Up here on holiday?

"Not really. We just live in Newcastle and have a caravan here. Been coming here for years. We love it. What did you say a 66 was?"

I am in such a good mood that I even offer

the flavour of all flavourings.

"*Do you want Monkey Blood with that?*"

Behind this friendliest of families, the queue is already beginning to stretch into the distance. Not sure if have enough churns to cope. My stomach is certainly churning in the excitement of it all. A visit to the factory for a quick re-fill could be on the cards. I just hope Jonny hasn't closed up shop for the day, I may need his help as I certainly wasn't expecting this. Days at the harbour begin much more leisurely. People tend to set up camp on the beach, take their dogs for a walk or set about launching their boats before they even think about having an ice cream. There seems to be a different culture in this little spot. I guess it is all down to the fact that it is a fairly lengthy hike from the car park to the beach. At least at Beadnell, the punters can never really lose sight of my van, I am nearly always in view, and they know I will be there for most of the day. They know my routine and I know their movements.

Here it seems everyone is desperate for an ice cream now. After leaving the grassy, car park spot, there will no way they will be popping back later. By the time they have collected their ice creams and taken them back to the beach they will have melted. No, this is the time. Get the goodies and drinks in now. No point in wasting time. It is a good start to the whole day beach experience for all they know, and I certainly haven't a clue, I may be here for only a few minutes. I am outside my comfort zone; this is new territory.

Then without warning it all kicks off and the sweet smell of sales quickly turns sour; the peace and tranquility is set to be shattered in a second. I am just serving the family with a 66 and all that when this huge figure appears right in front of the queue and right in front of me. The space between us is wafer thin. In fact, his nose is almost touching mine and I am sure it's not in a friendly Eskimo greeting kind of way.

There are various theories attached to this traditional Inuit greeting known as the Kunik. One, which seems to make the most sense, is they are so bundled up in at least ten layers of clothing to protect them from freezing temperatures, that the nose is the only part of the body exposed.

As this was not Alaska or Greenland, I readily assumed this man was not Nanook of the North but more like Bothered of Bamburgh.

He has a large moustache, a pristine white coat and a somewhat ruddy complexion. I don't think he is armed. Never thought to ask. He doesn't look happy. I have not seen him before and at this moment I don't really want to see him again. Probably not a man you would equate with a generosity of humour and a ready quip about a 66. No, I think he smells blood, and it is certainly not Monkey Blood.

"What do you think you are doing here?" he rages with a clenched fist.

Slightly alarming to say the least. Am I

hallucinating? Maybe it is one of those ghosts said to be knocking around from days gone by from Bamburgh Castle.

As for his enquiry. Pretty obvious I would have thought. Instead of saying something humorous like "*I am shearing sheep and making woolly hats,*" I just stumble a few words. I was sensing danger.

"*Just selling a bit of ice cream. Nice day again. Good spot.*"

"*You have no right to be here. This is my patch. If ever I see you again, I will give you a bloody nose. Get out of here now.*"

All this is blasted out in high decibels loud enough to scare the Puffins on the distant Farne Islands and even wake up the seals. This is not what I signed up for. No one warned me about the dune dangers, the skirmishes in the sand or the clash of the cones.

In a split second the queue has very quickly gone from very long to very short to no one at all. These people are here on holiday and don't want to be witness to a major crime scene.

Having to spend endless hours giving statements and then being asked to give testimony in court would cast a dark shadow over their sunny Northumberland days. I was half-expecting sirens, flashing blue lights and armed police to arrive.

"Ok. Put your 66's down. Move. Grab your kids and get to the beach. Don't worry no one will be harmed. You are all safe."

"Now, Mr Moustached Man, arms above your head. Drop to the ground. You are surrounded. There is no way out. Don't do anything silly. Just lie on the ground with your hands behind your back. Clearly where we can see them."

"Good man. Right don't move. No one gets hurt."

I may be exaggerating as in reality, not wanting to see any blood spilt, not even the monkey type, I sheepishly make a forlorn retreat and leave the few remaining would-be customers empty handed and a little shaken with ice cream replaced by *I scream*... No need for the riot squad. Not even those armed with milk crates and dustbin lids. I was off. Get me out of here as quickly as possible. No wonder I have not been here before. It is bandit country. Enter at your own risk. Trespassers will be executed. Maybe I just missed the signs.

I slide back the serving window in a flash, better have some protection, and jump into the driver's seat and switch on the engine. To say I sped off is a slight contortion of the truth as my van would be hard pushed to win a race with a snail from a standing start. But I do make my great escape with what is left of my pride, even though my hands are shaking, and my face is probably the colour of the vanilla ice cream I was so happy to be serving. I take a quick glance back and he is still standing there with his face even a deeper red, arm raised and fist waving. But there is no one around. He stands alone like a statue. A one-man protest with no one listening. Everyone has given him a wide berth and hurtled towards the beach or back to their cars. He looks like the scariest of scarecrows.

It is only then I notice he actually does have an ice cream van, now virtually the only vehicle left in a rapidly emptying car park. It looks fairly normal and a bit surprising as I was half-expecting it to be an armoured tank.

I am back on the main road to Seahouses and on the way back to the no man's land of Beadnell. On route I find a quiet spot for some much-needed rest and recuperation. I had got away without injury and at least I now have a good story to relate to *"you bugger I sold some pop"* and the rest of the gang in the morning.

I wonder if the scarecrow still standing where I left him, maybe waiting for other unsuspecting ice cream sellers. Has he moved? Will he stay like that for the rest of the summer? Or indeed, has he been rounded up, put in a churn and sent out to sea? He might be on his way to Norway. You know what, I really don't care.

I am already visualising the morning chat with colleagues.

"Have a good day yesterday?"

"A bit different. Nearly got beaten up by half-man half-walrus. It was slightly scary. Lost a lot of customers. Looks as though I strayed into enemy territory, but I didn't realise we had any enemies. He seemed a little perturbed that I had ventured into what he said was his patch and I was never to go there again. There was even a hint of violence."

"Never mind. Doesn't sound like much. Are you back down to the harbour today? Looks like another scorcher. Make sure you have plenty of ice cream on board. Have fun. But you bugger I sold some pop yesterday."

"Thanks. You guys too."

They probably won't be that bothered. Nothing seems to ruffle any feathers round here. It is all calm and crisis free. No need for confrontation. We are all in the same job and just get on with it. There is a sneaky suspicion, something not quite right in the sea air, that they all know this man and it is best I found out for myself in some kind of ghoulish initiation ceremony.

I did recount the tale to my employer later the same day. I wanted him to know exactly what happened and to know there was no intimidation or threatening behaviour on my part. Made sure there were no forms to fill in, no health and safety guidelines to follow and no need for a medical check-up. I also wanted to know the ground rules as to where I should, and more importantly, where I shouldn't be going. It was a long summer and I wanted to enjoy it. I suppose I was getting my retaliation in first in case there were any repercussions.

I needn't have worried. The boss was visibly perplexed and a little irritated by it all. "*What do you mean he said you can't go there? His patch? What utter nonsense. You can go exactly where you want. Next time you see him, just tell him that. You have much right to be there as he has. To be honest, I don't think you will be seeing much more of him. His bark is much bigger than his bite. All bravado, nothing else. Now get on and sell some ice cream. That's what I pay you for.*"

Message received. Loud and clear. It never happened again. I rarely ventured back into the badlands. All for a peaceful life and there are plenty of other places to go.

But the incident did at least provoke some childless and harmless retribution. Just a bit of fun. I linked up with my Shooting Star student pal from the fleet as some kind of Butch Cassidy and the Sundance Kid tribute act and set out in pursuit of our moustached villain.

Our cunning plan, especially when we are a bit bored, was to go out of our way to spot him and park our vans with one in front and one behind. A kind of ice cream van wafer. No nougat, no chocolate and no harm.

Don't worry it never escalated. We soon get fed up and I am sure he did. But this was not before we milked the situation and cornered him a few more times to show him the chimes are a' changing. He still seems to bare some kind of strange grudge. On the rare occasion our vans passed each other I am always greeted with a waved fist and a grimace. But it never goes further. There is really no need to speak to him.

We got friendly with another guy from the rival business and an erstwhile colleague of half man half walrus. He is as different as chalk and cheese, and you wouldn't think they were on the same team. Doesn't seem to have any particular territory. He is simply doing the same as us. A student earning an honest crust or least a tidy wafer. He is fairly laid back, virtually horizontal and probably the closest to cool I have ever come across. He has long hair, talks in kind of vague sentences where the words don't really go together and occasionally injects the word 'groovy' or 'wow' for no apparent reason. But a good cop compared to his bad cop partner. I never see the two of them together though. I couldn't really see them getting on. Moustached man doesn't strike me as that kind of groovy, peace loving and flowers in your hair type of guy.

Unfortunately for our cool rival, we discover

that after selling ice cream during the day he boosts his income as a part-time DJ at night at the local disco in Seahouses, spinning records and no doubt spinning a yarn to anyone bothered to listen. To make it even better he even has a turntable identity. He is Captain Fantastic.

Only been to the nightspot once. All a bit dark, a little bit dingy and to be honest, a little boring. Half the time it looked as though Captain Fantastic was talking, or shouting, to himself. The crowds weren't exactly flocking in or maybe it was just a quiet night when I was there. On other times they might be queuing round the block, maybe seals get cheap tickets and flop across from the Farnes for a change of scenery and a bit of flirting.

It was also the time when a typical Top of the Pops line-up included such delights as The Real Thing and Barry White, along with such oddities as David Dundas singing about putting his jeans on. Music probably best heard at a very low volume or really not at all.

Anyhow, Captain Fantastic was happy to tell us he was also known as Captain Fantastic. This was music to our ears and a fantastic bit of good fortune. It was only fair that other people knew the name. I have really no idea where he picked the name from and don't think he has either to be honest. It just suits him perfectly. Maybe me and my Bad Company loving colleague should call ourselves Batman and Robin and be general do-gooders saving the world with delicious ice cream.

Anyhow, after getting bored chasing Mr Moustache Man around, me and my fellow caped crusader have a bit more harmless fun. We regularly meet up with Captain Fantastic for the occasional bar meal or two as we don't really see him as the enemy. He is just an all-round good guy with confrontation as an alien concept.

When darkness is about to descend and the ice cream world has gone to sleep, the three of us occasionally meet up in a local bar in Bamburgh for a bit of rest and recuperation after a hard day at the office. As usual I take the orders, burgers and chips for all of us and go to the guy at the end of the bar to convey our needs and give our names. He is up for a bit of fun and readily agrees to calling out Captain Fantastic when his order is ready for collecting and taking back to our table.

It is really good tonight as the place is fairly packed and the orders, Smith, Jones, Clarke, Watson and so on, are regularly announced. The bar always seems to be quiet just at the time when the name Captain Fantastic is shouted out in high decibel fashion, raising much muffled laughter as Captain Fantastic himself ambles his way forward, resembling anything other than a superhero, and collects his burger and chips in a basket. It makes us laugh every time. It is just a shame he doesn't quickly put on a funny costume, fly across the bar and whizz up into the sky with his meal for one. Now that would be good.

***

As for moustached half-walrus man, I do manage to have the last laugh and ensure he gets nowhere near any of what I believe is my territory.

The territories in question are the two huge caravan sites that nestle just behind the beautiful Beadnell beach.

It is the place to be at the end of the day, especially if sales have been slow and the coffers almost empty. There are literally scores of families here, all desperately in search of that final ice cream. The caravans seem to stretch for miles. And they come in all shapes and sizes. Most are of the static variety and double as holiday homes.

Some have added little gardens, others have a bit of decking and outside seating. There are also an assortment of canoes and small boats stored under many of them. The flashier ones even have those annoying speed boats alongside.

Then there are the tourers. These are much

smaller and along with the tractors and lorries, they are the ones that clog up the roads every summer.

Just as you are driving quite happily up the A1 or indeed any other major in the country, the little tourer caravans are the ones that put the jam in the traffic. They are normally pulled by a car with enough wing mirrors to see faraway planets in high definition, but mysteriously have a blind spot when it comes to the queue of cars just behind. The driver, normally in a peaked hat, sunglasses and driving gloves, never has any intention of pulling across and letting you past.

No, when the summer arrives, they are the self-appointed rulers of the road. They make the rules and the rest just have to follow. This means going at a very leisurely pace. No need to rush. We are on holiday. Plenty of time to look at the scenery.

Well, you may not be in a hurry but the rest of us are. *Tough luck. Stay behind and come along for the ride. We are all going on a summer holiday.*

In the caravan sites here at Beadnell they mingle quite happily with their larger neighbours and help generate the hustle and bustle of a small town. These sites are a treasure trove for people like me. There are families everywhere and in the early evening all they seem to want is an ice cream.

If I make these sites my own, then my job is done every day. Sales will always be good. So, imagine my horror the first time I went in and saw moustached man just leaving. He had beaten me to it. This can't happen again. My nest egg is in danger of cracking or being poached.

So, let's be clever. I need the caravanners as my customers and mine alone. All I have to do is get them on my side. The alternative is to get there before my rival every night and follow him round. Even for my fairly low standards that would be fairly embarrassing. No one would win. The spoils would have to be shared and what is the point in that.

Getting there before him requires a degree of organisation and that is one word that will not be included in any future job references.

So after being blown out the previous night when he got there first, I decide to go back again the following evening with a different tactic. Once bitten and twice buy and all that. It is good fortune, good luck, or good timing as I have queues almost as long as the eye can see as soon as I arrive on site. My rival is either asleep, on a day off or a little late. Now I have the queues I have to keep them.

Freebies. Everyone likes something for nothing. I have loads of boxes of chocolate flakes for those wanting a 99 or the upside-down version. So why not just give them away as well. With virtually every sale I hand over extra flakes to share. It is like throwing confetti or coins at a wedding. There are kids scrambling everywhere. Some solutions are the simplest. I suppose it is a case having your flake and eating it.

And it works. I go back the very next night

and am slightly perturbed to see moustached man making his getaway. Maybe I have blown it. But no, they are all waiting for me and make a dash to the van as soon as the first chimes ring out.

"Come on. Flake man has arrived. Let's go!"

"You can have as many as you want. He throws them out the window. It's the best part of the day. That grumpy man with the moustache doesn't give anything away and he gives smaller portions. He's rubbish."

"Can we have some flakes please?"

"Of course. How many do you want? In fact, just wait, here's the box, just take as many as you want."

It even escalates with people appearing with vessels of all shapes and sizes. Buckets, pans, plates, jugs, bottles and bowls. They want family meals. Ice cream for everyone. Only too happy to oblige. I will put ice cream on a frying pan if I have to. Remember the customer is always right. I feel a bit like the Pied Piper. Wherever I go, others tend to follow.

It is now the same well-worn and successful script every night. The same story of soaring sales. I have fought him on the beaches, in the car parks and the caravan sites. I have never surrendered.

Never in the field of ice cream conflict has so much been owed by so many flakes to so few sales for my rival. I never saw half man half walrus on site again. Literally out of site out of mind.

Money, money, money. All the way round they wait. It is like a lap of honour every night. As long as I just turn up the sales keep coming. Happy days. Needless to say, I never tell the boss about the throwaway flakes.

He is just pleased to see huge wads of cash handed over every night. Though I suspect he thought something was up as I stacked boxes and boxes of flakes into the van every morning. He just smiles and counts the daily takings.

"Well done son. That's my boy. I knew you would make an ice cream man one day."

The Times They Are A'Changing

Time for a change today. Beadnell is my favourite spot. Sunshine, harbour, lime kilns, boats and beach. Not a bad office and not a bad way to spend summer days. It is a great place for the old ice cream business. Always plenty of people, plenty of customers and plenty of sales, except on the rare occasion when the sun decides to hide behind granite skies.

The van almost blocks the route to the beach. People have to come round it to get to the sand. It is strategic planning. With the beach as my window, the path to the harbour and lime kilns on the other side and the rambling street up into the village in the other direction, it is the perfect spot.

I do vary this and occasionally nip round to the car park that nestles just behind the beach a few hundred yards away. This is another pole position as I catch everyone either going or coming back from the beach. The best time to get here is around mid to late afternoon, the time of the day when many holiday makers are searching for an ice cream.

The parking spot is also just next to the path where a tractor is on hand to tow boats across the sands and into the water and the other way round when messing about on the water is complete. Unfortunately, most of the boats involved are those speedboats and the owners seem to enjoy being the focal point. They all wear the full wetsuit gear, talk loudly and generally stand around admiring each other, other boats and the size of their engines. On the rare occasions these guys order ice creams they tend to come to the hatch with the wetsuits peeled half-way down to expose their rotund stomachs. Not a pretty sight but who am I to judge as long as they buy something.

I could be judging them rather harshly. They are probably a harmless bunch and maybe being so loud comes courtesy of having to talk over those loud engines all the time. We never have much banter.

All the other cars in the park belong to families all set for a day out and they are my really valuable, and often repeat customers. I probably sell more here than I do round by the harbour, but the view is nowhere near as good, and I do miss that.

But you can have too much of a good thing. Always leave them wanting more. They will be even more pleased to see you when you are back. So today it is bye bye Beadnell and on course for Craster.

Craster is a quaint fishing village not that far away from Beadnell. Yes, another quaint spot, but we are rather spoilt round here. This one lacks the hustle and bustle of a Beadnell or a Seahouses but has its own special charm. It is a short trip down south from Seahouses, about 20 to 25 minutes away and it has to be the best coastal walk on the planet.

It is a short two-mile stroll leading out of the village along a well-worn path that clings to the rocky coastline and ends at the magnificent ruins of Dunstanburgh Castle. And you can't really get lost. It is flat, straight and easy. Even on a foggy day you could still find the castle and your way back without falling into the sea.

The castle has seen better days. In that estate agent speak again it would be described as '*a must-see, desirable residence in a much sought-after area. Plenty of scope for redevelopment or use as holiday home. Complete with spectacular views. Viewing by appointment only.*'

It sits just above a vast and steep sided gulley, enough to warn off any would-be attackers and a landing that even our own Grace Darling would probably think twice about attempting. If you ever managed to get a boat near, you would then be faced with an almost impossible scramble up the cliffs and the guys at the top just laughing as they poured burning oil down or emptied the bins right on top of you. Come to think of it, Monkey Blood would be great weapon to ward off would-be attackers. That would be a bloody battle.

The guidebooks tell us Dunstanburgh Castle was built at a time when relations between King Edward II and his most powerful baron, Earl Thomas of Lancaster, had become openly hostile. Lancaster began the fortress in 1313, and the latest archaeological research indicates that he built it on a far grander scale than was originally planned, perhaps more as a symbol of his opposition to the king than as a military stronghold.

It didn't end well for the Earl. His rebellion was defeated and he was executed in 1322. It was then passed to someone known as John of Gaunty, or was it a thin man known as gaunt John? In an attempt to defend off any rampaging Scots the twin towered gatehouse was converted into a keep.

It later became the focus of fierce fighting during the Wars of the Roses. It was twice besieged and captured by Yorkist forces, before it decayed into the ruins we see today. And as ruins go, they are certainly worth seeing. Very evocative of a bygone age and testament to the ravages of many a battle. They almost look like someone has sketched them onto the landscape as they tumble out from the ground in a last defiant act.

The entrance is a puzzle. There is a large and locked wooden gate with a much smaller swing through gate at one end to gain access, then you have to take a few steps up a graveled path and into the ruins. If you were a cheapskate, then you could easily wander round the castle for free. It takes a bit of time and intuition to stumble across the kiosk where you buy a ticket, pick up a guidebook and buy a souvenir fridge magnet or a tea towel with those Puffins. You could just as easily walk straight past it, and no one checks if you have a ticket or not.

I have done that on occasions. I suppose I do work round here so I do contribute to the local economy in other ways. Just wondering round the castle with the sharp drop to the sea and the silhouetted ruins is a marvelous experience; you can just imagine it in the olden days. You can almost hear the swords clashing and the arrows landing.

It is then a return walk, hopefully not with the wind blowing straight in your face to make it a little more testing. At the other end, back in Craster, you can nip into the local pub for some delightful crab soup or crab sandwiches. Delicious. Tasting all the better when you gaze out across the North Sea.

I normally park the van just above the harbour. That is where I am today. It is a strategic spot as it grabs castle walkers at the start or on their way back and also those venturing up the hill to grab a kipper or at least to smell one or two. This is the land of the famous Craster Kipper. They have been smoked here for more than a hundred years. Smoking a kipper is not the same as smoking a cigarette. The vision of people wandering into the local shop and asking for 20 kippers rather than 20 Woodbine is just a weird picture, as unlikely as walking across to the castle with a lighted kipper in your mouth and clouds of smoke rising above your head.

The real explanation is slightly more straightforward. A kipper is a silver darling of the sea, a herring, carefully and lovingly hung above fires in a smokehouse. Years ago they were split by hand by herring girls, but now this is mostly done my machine. They are then placed in a brine solution of plain salt and water and hung up on what are known as tenterhooks.

Fires made from whitewood shavings and oak sawdust are placed under the rows of herring; these smoulder away for at least sixteen hours before the kippers are ready.

The smokehouse has been in the hands of several generations of the same family for years and years. The kippers do smell but they are delicious, especially if poached or grilled with a side plate of hot buttered toast and a squeeze of lemon.

That smell does linger. I can vouch for that. I have made the schoolboy error of buying a few, wrapping them in newspaper, and taking them back to the van with a view to having them for a meal either later that day or for tomorrow's breakfast. The stink is horrendous. It is long and lasting. There is no air freshener, disinfectant or cleaning fluid in the world that can get rid of it. They put the linger in lingering. The distinct aroma can last for days. But don't let the smell put you off the taste. They are a great meal.

Also don't get mixed up with the mysteriously fashionable kipper ties. These are very large and very wide, indeed kipper shaped, and come in a variety of garish colours that don't match. They almost look like you are wearing a tent round your neck, winding them round your collar and attempting some kind of knot takes about four days.

No kippers in the van today. I haven't really had the time to nip up the hill and get some.

Having kippers in the van has me on tenterhooks as well. A tenter refers to a wooden frame, often a line of fencing that was used to hang woolen or linen cloth to prevent it from shrinking as it dries. The tenterhooks are the hooks on the tenter used to hold the cloth, or in this case the herring, in place. The phrase 'on tenterhooks' came to mean being in a state of tension, uneasiness, anxiety or suspense, just like the cloth on the tenter.

It's a great phrase. Just like 'don't put all your eggs in one basket' or 'don't count your chickens before they hatch.' No idea where they came from. Probably not anything to do with Craster, herring or kippers. Or I could be barking up the wrong tree. Never mind, we will cross that bridge when we come to it.

It is a good day though. Sales are brisk rather than busy. Plenty of time to listen to the radio and even turn a page or two on the book. By the end of the summer, I may have even finished it.

The walkers are a cheery lot. Always happy

to chat. You can see them coming a mile off. Many have maps rounds their necks, tangling with binoculars, and about five pairs of really thick socks protruding halfway up their legs from sensible hiking boots. I bet some of them just put all this clobber and don't even hike across to the castle; they just nip straight to the pub and tuck into the crab. I am more than happy to point them in this direction or up to the smokehouse. It only seems fair that I play my part and help other businesses out. We are all very friendly round here. I consider myself almost a local.

Craster has its own unique charm. Quiet but mysterious and never really very busy. The neat row of houses that line-up just above and away from the harbor, always look warm and inviting. Parking a car does seem to be a problem though. As I have this prime slot just above the harbor, I can watch them circling round each other trying to find a space in some kind of coastal dance.

There is a car park, just on the right as you

come into Craster, which was formerly a quarry. At the end of the harbour there is what remains of rather tall and somewhat ugly structure that was originally used to lift stone from the quarry and onto boats to be shipped to London. Here it was used for kerbstones. Paving the way for success you could say.

Craster – the gateway to kippers and kerbstones. That should be on the entrance sign to the village. It would certainly attract a lot more attention and make for great souvenir tee-shirts, postcards and even silly hats.

I have only just thought of that as I gaze down across the sea with the majestic ruins of Dunstanburgh Castle just visible the other way. It is a very tranquil setting. I do pop along here now and again as a change of scenery is always good for the soul. But sometimes I feel I am trespassing. I don't know why; it is not as though someone is going to come along and slap me in the face with a kipper or drop a kerbstone on my head. I just feel Craster, maybe, has its own rules and they are only known about if you are from this little part of the world. By all means come along and enjoy the kippers, the crabs and the castle, but just don't stay too long. I could be completely wrong. It still doesn't stop me from coming back, as I do enjoy it.

The harbour itself always seems to be eerily quiet. There a couple of fishing boats on the rocks leading down to the sea, a few scattered lobster pots, the odd bits of rope lying around here and there and occasionally someone fishing off the end of the pier. But all in all, it has far less bustle than the busier neighbours at Beadnell and Seahouses. There are never many boats around.

Even in the winter this is a great place to visit. A walk on the wild side to the castle and back in fiercely cold winds is invigorating and uplifting and guaranteed to make your cheeks the rosiest they have ever been. Cap it all off with a crab sandwich round a roaring open fire in the local pub and you could be in heaven. Those short days and low temperatures seem a world away at the moment as I need to make hay while the sun still shines. Another curious phrase but one that seems very appropriate at this precise moment.

There has been a steady stream of customers, a good day, good sales and good banter but my frenzied chocolate flake bonanza is on the horizon, and I need to get off to the treasure trove around the caravan sites at Beadnell. They will be expecting me.

***

Before I get back to Beadnell I decide to make a slight detour and drop into Embleton, just a couple of miles up the road from Craster.

This is a place I find really hard to define. It always seems slightly desolate, empty, and lacking soul. You half expect to see tumbleweed rolling down the road and figures from the past shuffling around without making a sound.

I pull up in what I suppose you call the centre of this tiny hamlet. There is a large hotel on one side, a small stretch of grass and a shop. There is no one here, no point in sticking around. No one in search of an ice cream. If I set the chimes off the locals may think it is an air raid siren and scuttle even further into their homes or scramble into underground shelters. No need to disturb the sound of silence. People talking without speaking. People listening without hearing.

After pausing for a few moments, I start up the old van and make the way up the hill which makes way for a marvelous view of the North Sea, the grassy dunes and the glorious ruins of Dunstanburgh Castle in the distance. From here the road narrows into a tiny lane which slopes all the way down to the golf course and a path across the fairways to the beach.

I drive down the lane to the wooden shed that is the clubhouse and park just outside, then amble across to the seashore for a sneaky break. It is always good to stretch the legs and unfurl myself from the daily bending over to reach into the churns. The sands seem to stretch for miles but there is hardly anyone here as I go past the haunted frightened trees out to the windy beach.

At the opposite end to the castle, the beach comes to a halt and is overshadowed by a high grassy knoll with a spattering of tiny timber cottages that must have some of the best sea views anywhere. They have no electricity or running water and to get there, it's a long trek from the golf clubhouse and a steep stroll to the top. Even carrying all your worldly goods, the journey must be worth it as the destination is unique.

Round the other side of all this is Low Newton, another lovely beach stretches out to a lovely little village at Newton-by-the-Sea, with a cluster of houses surrounding a pub. I have never actually been round there selling ice cream. Could be missing a honey pot but the roads are very narrow and not the best place to park my van and obstruct everybody.

I should probably get back to work and get back to Beadnell. It is late afternoon as the sun is already beginning to set. It does appear that the days are shorter in Embleton; it appears to be the kind of place that embraces the dark side of the world. My van grinds back up the hill to the centre of the village and there is still hardly anyone around. All very strange and I really can't make my mind up, is it really just a sleepy satellite on the surface of the Northumberland coast or something slightly more sinister? There are a few houses and some delightful cottages straddled across the tiny circumference and I am sure it is a nice place to live or have a holiday home, but it is just so quiet. It has the atmosphere of an elderly resting home with a pace of life slower than sedate.

Hard to believe that an old whinstone quarry just to the north was in action for nearly 100 years until it closed in 1961 and at times provided employment for up to 80 men.

Just after the First World War the whole place was thriving. There were apparently two butcher shops, three grocers and baker's shops, two blacksmiths with at least one smithy, some four milk suppliers, a tailor, a boot and shoemaker, two dressmakers, two joiners, several general contractors and a policeman complete with police station.

Now, there appears to be just one shop, a couple of pubs and the rather grand Dunstanburgh Castle Hotel. I have never been in the hotel or indeed seen anyone either going in or out, but I am reliably informed it is very popular. Maybe all my visits to Embleton have coincided with some kind of siesta; it is a place that does seem to put sleeping as a priority.

As I say I could be sullying the good name and the good people of Embleton. I do apologise if this is the case. I do recommend a trip to the spectacular sands and the golf course is very picturesque and no doubt very challenging. It is another stunning part of Northumberland but just not the place for me.

Not much chance of 66's and 99's making up the numbers or Monkey Blood making a comeback. I fear if I stay here too long, I may also fall asleep myself.

Time to leave and get back and mine the rich seams of the Beadnell caravan sites. Getting there is a torturous route along a long and winding road with many turns, sharp bends and narrow gauges to negotiate. But I know it will be worth it. Getting back to my home base will be a much-needed boost from the soporific but very quaint Embleton. I did enjoy Craster though. Always good to pop along there, always plenty of customers, always worth the kippers and the views. A change is always as good as a rest and I do feel I have benefitted from varying my route.

This red-hot summer just presents too many good opportunities not to be missed. It is days like this I feel sorry for my colleagues who are stuck in those static selling points at Seahouses harbour or the car park in Bamburgh. It is up to me if I want to change the scenery, as I can always move along to somewhere different and the Northumberland coast never lets me down. Always something different to see and do. It is a moving vista. Sands and seals to castles, crabs, kippers and commanding views. I am just lucky to be here. The weather is great, sales are going along nicely, and the company and camaraderie is all good. It is already turning into a glorious summer on all accounts. My boss seems happy with my work, the old van has only stumbled to a halt a couple of times and I have not made any mistakes, well not to date anyhow. I am sure there is time for my complacency to be disturbed.

No Ice Cream Today

I am not working today. Nearly always welcome. It is always strange waking up and suddenly realising I will not be making that short trip to Seahouses, chatting with the gang and selling ice cream for hours on end. I do confess that six days a week can be quite strenuous. We all need a break now and again; I do miss meeting up with my ice cream colleagues and getting all the latest gossip. But my back does need a rest and my vocal chords, suffering from hours of endless and often inane chat with customers, need some time-off.

It is always difficult to decide exactly what to do. Sometimes it is tempting to get in the car and nip back down to Newcastle to get a good meal and a bit of washing done. As this means a round trip of nearly 100 miles, it is rarely undertaken.

No, today is all about leisure. The most physical effort of the day is required in actually getting up and sorting the bed out to become a table again and for the caravan to look like a respectable living area. Space is quite tight, so I virtually roll onto the tiny space of floor that is left, pull the sleeping bag and blankets with me and then start sliding. It involves the tricky but well-practiced routine of sliding what was the bed sideways and then sliding up other sections into what miraculously forms a table with enough seating for four.

Then, the sleeping bag and whatever blankets and pillows I have, are then thrown next to the table, immediately reducing the seating to just two and I get dressed before pulling back the curtains.

I could have stayed in bed a bit longer but the sun is already turning up the heat on what is going to be, yet another glorious day and it would seem a shame to waste it. Occasionally I wish the blue would turn to grey, the heavens open and a great deluge descend. Firstly, this would give me an excuse to stay in bed and do absolutely nothing and secondly with the weather being so bad it would mean I was not missing a glorious ice cream selling day and making some money.

I turn on the radio. I am addicted to the radio as I may have mentioned. It is great source of everything from news and sport to comedy and music and everything in between. You name it. It is just wonderful. How come someone sitting in London can be speaking to me in Beadnell and giving me all the latest news or a running commentary on the latest big sporting event is all just magical. It is a very intimate dialogue. The person on the radio always feels like they are speaking just to me. How does that work? Go on, you don't really know do you and I certainly don't have a clue, I am just glad it does, and I have not run out of batteries yet.

No doubt some clever clog will tell me it all works by transmitting and receiving electromagnetic waves. The radio signal is an electronic current moving back and forth very quickly. A transmitter radiates this field outward via an antenna; a receiver then picks up the field and translates it to the sounds heard through the radio.

Science was not my favourite topic at school. I was put off by my chemistry teacher. If I didn't understand something and said something like *"why is that litmus paper changing colour?"* He would simply reply *"you tell me."* Well, if I knew I wouldn't have asked the question in the first place. I soon stopped asking questions and just sat at the back turning the Bunsen burner on and off. The only litmus tests these days is how much ice cream I sell.

As I switch the radio on, I hear that Great Britain and Iceland have decided to end the cod war, although I am not really sure what all the fuss is about, Queen's epic single Bohemian Rhapsody has gone gold and Mike Brearley is about to make his test debut against the West Indies. There you are—three interesting facts in three minutes. I do try and be clever sometimes and slip in the odd nugget when I am selling a 99 and a nougat wafer. Maybe I should call them nugget wafers. Every one comes with the latest news.

"*Morning, another nice day. See Brearley gets his first England cap today. Wonder how he will get on. Should be a firm pitch. Rather him than me facing those West Indians bowling at 80mph from just 22 yards away and I thought selling ice cream was tricky enough.*"

"*Anyhow look on the bright side, everyone has seen sense in that little cod disagreement between us an Iceland. Not sure what all the fuss is about. Plenty more fish in the sea if you ask me.*"

"*And how about that Queen song? It seems to last for about an hour and I have no idea what it means but it is really good. What do you think? No doubt it will be on the radio again today. It will probably come on after this and finish when I go home for the night. But that Freddie Mercury is a bit of a genius don't you think? Even more complicated than Bob Dylan but that's another story.*"

"Anyhow, there you go, one 99 and one nougat wafer, enjoy. Thanks. Might see you later."

The opening lyrics to Bohemian Rhapsody always seem a fitting commentary to my life as an ice cream man.

Is this the real life
Is this just fantasy
Caught in a landside
No escape from reality
Open your eyes,
Look up to the skies and see,
I'm just a poor boy, I need no sympathy,
Because I'm easy come, easy go,
Little high, little low,
Any way the wind blows doesn't really matter to
Me, to me

Then it gets a bit deep and philosophical before crashing into

I see a little silhouetto of a man,
Scaramouch, Scaramouch, will you do the

Fandango!

Thunderbolts and lightning, very, very frightening me

Galileo, Galileo

Galileo, Galileo

Galileo, Figaro – magnifico

Great stuff. I always turn it up loud when it comes on, makes for great listening and good conversation.

"No, I have no idea what it is about either. It is very clever though. Like an Opera without the boring bits."

It actually topped the UK singles chart for nine weeks. Interesting it was eventually knocked off the lofty perch by a song by something slightly shallower. Mama Mia by Abba.

The masterful, if ludicrous, six-minute suite of operatic rock about a man who killed someone, sold his soul to Beelzebub and wants to know if Scaramouche can do the Fandango , was overtaken by...

Mamma Mia here I go again
My, my how can I resist you?
Mamma Mia does it show again
My, my just how much I've missed you

Isn't that just why the great British public are so fascinating. How come Queen can be flavour of the month one week and Abba the next? As my brother once said: "*It is great we all have different tastes or there would no need for boxes of mixed biscuits.*" Can't get much deeper than that.

Suppose it is a bit similar in the ice cream world. Bit boring if everyone just liked 99's and nothing else. How would "*bugger I sold some pop*" do and would there be enough chocolate flakes for everyone.

After a quick shower at the nearby block which resembles more Cell Block H than luxury, it is a quick bowl of cereal and off to the local shop. It is just great in here. It is bang in the middle of the village, right opposite the pub, and just a couple of minutes from the caravan.

It is just about as chaotic as the gift shop in Seahouses. There are several rows of high stacked shelving which stand side by side leaving little space for actually getting around. They also seem to wobble after the slightest of contact. There is everything in here from Creamola Foam and cornflakes to Dandelion and Burdock and dairy milk chocolate.

I am told Dandelion and Burdock has been drunk in this country since the Middle Ages. It was originally a type of light mead, but over the years evolved into a carbonated soft drink. The marketing speak tells us that the drink has an interesting blend of liquorice and aniseed, infused with dandelion and burdock roots as well as other herbal extracts. Personally, I think car engine oil would taste better and probably be more refreshing.

I always think this village store is a bit of a shoplifter's paradise. You could easily conceal a can of beans up your jumper or bag some biscuits as the sales counter is at the far end and often difficult to see as it is surrounded by so many people. Of course, I have never given occasional theft an occasional thought. I belong to the community now and this is another business I am happy to support.

I grab a bits and bobs to keep me going, tea bags, digestives, marmalade, newspaper and bread and do my honest duties—present them for payment. Next to the till is a cleverly positioned pile of fresh morning rolls and I add three to my basket. It is always really friendly in here, a lovely sense of summer where everybody just seems happy to be here. There is no rush, plenty of time to idly chat the time of day away. I occasionally do get spotted and recognised.

"Not in the ice cream van today then. Pity really as it looks set for another blistering day. Can you remind what 66's are as my kids would love to try them. Not sure about all that Monkey Blood though. Anyhow, need to get everyone rounded up for the beach. Catch-up sometime. Have fun. Do you need any more

rolls? They were freshly made this morning. Just the job. I see Queen are no longer top of the pops. Great song. No idea what it is about though."

Back to the caravan then. This is probably the most enjoyable thirty minutes of the week. No work, a leisurely cup of tea, bacon sandwich and good read of the newspaper, all accompanied by some background noise from the radio. I always look at the sports pages first but not much happening on the Newcastle United front as the new season is still weeks away and the players are on holiday. You could have said they were already on holiday when they lost the League Cup final. Dreaming more of the beach than lifting a trophy.

I might go for a little stroll. I go across the fields, pass the deep quarry pond, through the first of the large caravan sites and onto the beach. Of course I grab a quick glance at the car park and then from the sand I can see the harbour. No one there. There is always the nightmare that moustached man may have taken my place or even a completely new interloper. Always good to see my turf, my manor, remains uninhabited.

I walk round the harbour, past the lime kilns and onto a small path that takes me past the sailing club, some fantastic little cottages with sea views and out onto what is locally called the point, a rocky outcrop that stretches out to the sea.

If you look carefully, and I mean very carefully, there are some grassy lumps and bumps and what looks like a tiny crater. It is said to be the remains of a 12th or 13th century chapel named after St Ebba or Ebba, a Northumbrian princess. It is surrounded by some earthworks which are believed to be the remnants of an old monastery. These monks get everywhere around here. Still, if you want some peace and tranquility this would have been a great place to live.

Today, there are a couple of optimistic fishermen casting their long lines out into the crashing waters. I never see them catch anything. Still, it must be a nice way to spend the day. Just the sound of the sea and seagulls for company and the outside chance you may haul in something for supper.

I like just standing here. Your mind can drift and you can almost imagine the monks wandering past in silence contemplation. Makes you think what they did all day and how they survived. Still, it was their choice and their way of life. A much simpler life than we have today. I bet they would be horrified that only yards away from their base in years to come would be a man offering Monkey Blood to people. It does sound Pagan, some kind of ancient cleansing or paying for your sins.

"Take this man away and cover him in the blood of a monkey. He spoke at breakfast yesterday and annoyed the rest of us who have been silent all these years. And what he was saying wasn't very interesting. He said his porridge was cold and it was someone else's turn to clean and cook tomorrow, he was fed up doing it all. Others should step up to the

mark."

The Point was probably the ideal place for a monastery. For a start it is totally isolated, lovely views and the only invaders are likely to be swooping seagulls. Also, the monks may have decided to plonk themselves here as a great setting to find the meaning of life. It is such a lovely environment and does allow pause for thought.

I leave the rocky outcrop and meander my way up Harbour Road leading back to the village. On my left is a farm which is always knee deep in cow manure and making an interesting cocktail when combined with the smell of seaweed. I wonder if the cows like living here. Being next to the sea must make it quite idyllic, though I never seen them swimming or having an ice cream. I always think the farmer, like the rest of the locals, breathes a sigh of relief when summer comes to an end and the hordes depart. I say hordes but to be fair it never really gets that busy. There are always enough people around to keep ice cream sales ticking over and enough space for us all. You always get the feeling that people are just happy to be here. No kiss-me-quick hats or candy floss. There seems to be a mutual respect between the natural environment and the visitors. We want you here, not in huge numbers, enjoy yourselves and take care.

It is hard to imagine the fishermen's houses that nestle alongside the holiday homes on Harbour Road ever being replaced by Costa Del Sol type hotels, creating huge shadows on an unblemished seafront, and having rows and rows of neatly assembled sunbeds stretching around Beadnell beach and your personal space being invaded by barefoot traders trying to sell unwanted trinkets.

No, please stay like this.

It is late morning, and the trickle of beach dwellers has turned into a torrent as I go against the tide as they make their way past me. It is a great atmosphere. As I near the little shop at the entrance to the village I find a bench and sit down. The occasional person does nod in recognition and disappointment as I pass on the news it is my day off. Normal service will be resumed tomorrow.

I know some of the residents on Harbour Road, near the harbour end, have been getting views they didn't really want in recent days as lots of deep-sea divers park up, strip off with birthday suits before wetsuits. The bare faced cheek of it all. After looking for lobsters and wrecks they then come back and peel off their gear, hiding nothing, and back into their everyday clobber. Not exactly the rooms with views you would be expecting when having a lovely house overlooking the sea. Bit of a bum deal.

Apparently, there is actually believed to be a pile of treasure just off the Point that has yet to be discovered. In 1941 it rained money when the cargo ship the Somali exploded and the ship's safe has never been found. Shortly after 11:00 in the morning startled Beadnell villagers ran for cover as a spectacular shower of silver and copper coins poured down and set about a frantic scramble to grab the pennies from heaven.

The children of the village were the first on the scene only to find they literally got their fingers burnt by helping themselves to the cash as the coins were red hot.

That didn't stop the crafty kids profiting from the explosion though. They helped themselves to handfuls of the wet banknotes being washed onto the beach.

The previous day, the 6800-ton freighter, en route for Hong Kong, had taken three direct hits from a squadron of German Heinkel 111 bombers.

The seventy crew and thirty-eight passengers survived but, after they were rescued, a decision was taken to cast the ship adrift in the hope that the raging fires would burn themselves out. A tug was dispatched to attach a line to try to beach the Somali, but it exploded before the towboat arrived.

Within five minutes the Somali sunk to the

seabed. The money was destined for Hong Kong along with a variety of other items, including lorry tyres, ammunition, batteries, shoes, medical supplies, mercury, hay and a ton of miniature lead soldiers.

The wreck of the ship will never be left in peace until one lucky diver finds the missing currency and safe and trousers all the money that is still to be found. I might have a dive down myself one day.

The rest of the day is spent sitting outside the caravan, reading a book and then off to the back bar of the Beadnell Hall Hotel for an early evening snack, a sneaky beer and a quick catch-up with some of the locals. Then it is off to bed. It is work tomorrow.

Hitting The High Notes

There's a bit in the film Kelly's Heroes where Donald Sutherland leads his tanks into battle playing loud music. It's a cracking scene in an absolutely brilliant film with Clint Eastwood and Telly Savalas. I am not a film buff but I highly recommend this one. All about a ragged band of soldiers who go in search of millions of dollars of gold hidden in a bank behind enemy lines in World War Two.

It has also got some great music. 'Burning Bridges' by the Mike Curb Congregation is a classic opening sequence. You may think I have gone off piste again. No there is method in my madness. There is a theme here. When I go into ice cream battle there is bloodshed. It may be only Monkey Blood, but it is still a battle out there and I do play music.

In common with thousands of other ice cream vans across the country and many parts of the globe, I do have my own signature tune.

Admittedly they are referred to as chimes and I have no choice in the matter. If I did, it would be something witty or catchy. The Match of the Day theme would be good. I wouldn't mind a bit of Burning Bridges or maybe something more appropriate like the Beatles 'Here Comes the Sun'. But no, I am stuck with The Happy Wanderer.

Come on sing along...

I love to go a-wandering
Along the mountain track
And as I go, I love to sing
My knapsack on my back
Val-deri, val-dera
Val-deri, val-dera
Ha, ha, ha, ha, ha, ha
Ha
Val-dera
My knapsack on my back.

Mercifully my chimes come without lyrics and I rarely start them up. Well actually, all I have to is wind a button, yes seriously, and on they come. Interestingly not always at the same speed. Sometimes they come out more like some funeral dirge and at others resembling the soundtrack to a Benny Hill sketch.

Not sure they actually attract anyone although many people seem to stare in bewilderment as I trundle past. The old story goes of the mum telling her kids that when the chimes sound on an ice van it means all the ice cream has gone. A cunning and cost saving trick. I am sure good folk of Beadnell, Bamburgh and surrounding areas would never steep so low.

Some more trivia. Apparently Greensleeves is the most used ice cream van jingle. Though jingle is stretching it a bit. It is not exactly upbeat. Why a traditional folk song that could or could not have been written by Henry VIII and no one knows what it means, is top of the ice cream chimes, is an absurd bit of nonsense. It even blasts out from ice cream vans in Australia, India, New Zealand and South Africa.

Harry Burt is the man responsible apparently. Way back when, the 1950s or thereabouts, the man from Ohio added sleigh bells to his trucks to announce his arrival. They were so successful that he added them to a further twelve vehicles in his fleet.

Not sure sleigh bells in summer in Northumberland would give out the right message. Still keen on Match of the Day or the Stripper would be a laugh. Even a bit of Bob Dylan would be good, but no one would guess it is Dylan on the chimes or indeed the chimes are a changing.

Match of the Day was the first regular football programme on television and started in August 1964. The identity of the match, Liverpool v Arsenal, was kept secret until 4pm by agreement with the Football League who feared crowds would stay at home to watch it later.

I really only play 'The Happy Wanderer'

when I am on the caravan sites at night. Even then it is only sporadic. Heaven knows the tune annoys me and I don't want to do anything that outstays my welcome. There could be some exhausted mums trying to get their toddlers to sleep. They won't thank me for setting off the alarm bells and raising the wee ones from their slumber.

But it does serve a purpose and does get people to notice I am around. To date I have had no complaints about the sound. I do still hear it when I go to sleep at night and have caught myself humming it aloud while serving customers. Maybe on my last day I will slip in that Match of the Day tune, my own fanfare to the end of a glorious season.

An alternative would be one of those megaphones you see strapped to the top of cars at election times with candidates screeching out, often inaudibly, for people to vote for them.

"Hello, I am Fred Smotherwick your local

Conservative candidate in the general election. Please come out and vote for me on Thursday 6th May. I will look after you, fix your roads, collect your bins, get you a job and put you first. Come on. Your vote counts. Make it count for me"

This seems to be repeatedly endlessly and as the car never stops, you never have any time to have a proper look or ask any searching questions. For all you know it may not be even a real person in the car or the real candidate. And it is funny they always seem to appear in the street just as you trying to watch your favorite television programme, or the neighbours are trying to put their kids to bed. I always think it is a bit of pointless exercise. You can't hear what they are saying, no one really listens and hardly anyone cares. I don't think a quick blast of inane messaging is likely to persuade many voters. Most people have already made their mind up.

Still, I could link my on-board sound system to the sound of my own voice and maybe tell a few jokes.

"Hi. Your favourite ice cream man here. You know you want a 99. Just stop me. By the way did you know I have a pet newt called Tiny? Why is it called Tiny, I hear you say? Because it is my newt!!"

"Why did the chewing gum cross the road? It was stuck to the chicken's foot."

"I am here all summer."

By the way did you know the... *"Why did the chicken cross the road?"* is a common riddle joke, with the answer being... *"to get to the other side"* is an example of anti-humour, in that the curious setup of the joke leads the listener to expect a traditional punch line. There are better jokes around, and I must keep telling my customers some of them. Anything is better than *"what is a 66, an upside down 99?"*

Okay I will just stick to the tried and tested for the time being. The Happy Wanderer will continue to be my theme for the rest of the summer. Somehow it seems to fit perfectly if not always at the right speed...

**

I love this job. To coin a Roger Miller phrase: *'I'm a man of means by no means, king of the road.'* I can go where I want, do what I want, start and finish when I want and no one seems to really care.

Well maybe the boss does. But to be fair he rarely interferes. Ice cream out and money in, he's happy. It really is great freedom and I suppose the only way you could get sacked would either driving the van off the harbour into the sea, not turning up or selling nothing—even then you would probably get a second chance.

"You are not the first to end up in the sea and I sure you won't be the last. Just remember to keep the handbrake on when you are stopped, don't take any wrong turns and keep selling the occasional 66. It is not rocket science. You are not flying to the moon. Keep it

simple and then everyone is happy. By the way you may need a bigger bucket to get rid of all that water."

This really is a great way to spend the summer. Sometimes I have to pinch myself it is really happening; I even like hearing the seagulls when I arrive in Seahouses every morning, they are the sounds of the season...

They tell me I am at the seaside, and I can almost smell the fish and chips. They tend to circle, not knowing whether to swoop or not. They have never glided down on me. I just know I love having them around.

I often think, where do they come from? Where do they sleep and what are they saying to each other? As they are very noisy.

Here in Seahouses it is probably.

"Morning everybody. How are you doing?"

"I see they are loading up the ice cream vans again. Can't wait for the boat trips to the Farne islands to start. Always a lot of food round then. Those guys with the telescopes and binoculars often have lots of sandwiches. Wait

'til those terns start pecking their heads."

"We should have a bit of fun and join in one day."

"We had a great day yesterday, loads of people throwing chips everywhere. Another feast. Mind you, I need to cut down a bit. Putting on a bit of weight."

"Also hear there are a couple of trawlers due back in harbour soon. Even more food. I will check out the times. Let you know."

"Anyhow I must go now. Need to fly around in circles for a few hours and make a lot of noise. It's what the tourist seems to like. They know they must be near the sea if we are here."

"Have fun guys. See you later."

A bit of ornithology for you. We should not really refer to them as seagulls, the generic term is gulls, and all gulls belong to a widespread family of seabirds. They are mistakenly often known as seagulls, although no species is actually called a seagull and many are found far from the sea. They do get a bad reputation for stealing chips but are generally intelligent, adaptable and likeable birds but with so many different types they are incredibly difficult to identify. Entire books have been dedicated to telling one gull from another, but even these barely scratch the surface. Their plumage changes as they age and there's a great deal of variation within species.

Just to name a few we have Greater Black-Backed Gulls, Herring Gulls, Black-headed Gulls or just the common gull. No wonder they are easier named just seagulls. It makes life so much simpler.

In idle moments I often look up in the skies or across the beach and see if I can tell one gull from another. No, virtually impossible unless you are a busy birdwatcher—a wildlife expert. No, along with almost everyone round here I am more than happy just to call them seagulls. I am by the sea, there are lots of gulls around so they must be seagulls. Simple as that.

I know around here they just want to have fun, tease the trippers and get a bite to eat. They talk very loudly; let you know they are around and generally seem to be up for a bit of gentle amusement. They must have a great sense of humour and most don't even live here. They fly in from elsewhere just to be here and then fly back home a few weeks later. You just wonder if the word has got round that Seahouses is a good place to be in the summer. Lots of fishing boats, lots of fish and chips and some really invigorating sea air and spectacular scenery. Lots of tourists to tease, a great gift shop, good pubs, and delicious ice cream. Who wouldn't want to be here?

I know to some people seagulls can be annoying. Constantly squawking and swooping and occasionally leaving you with a little and unwanted messy present. But without them around it just wouldn't be the seaside. They would be missed.

Seahouses is more than seagulls. As already noted, it is not Blackpool. And that is just fine.

As I look across from where I am loading the van there are some interesting little oddities.

First of all, there is the ever-popular amusement arcade. If you have any loose change then that is the place to get rid of it quickly. There are plenty of opportunities. For instance, there is the glass cage where you put money in the slot and take control of a crane like object to try and grab an assortment of prizes. Well, complete junk to be more exact. The fact that it will never have enough grip to actually take anything and is too small to grab the large objects, is almost immaterial. You know it won't work but you still do it.

The so-called prizes are not worth anything. What would you do with a fluffy ball or a miniature set of playing cards? Throw them away most likely. Even the plastic key rings look decidedly unusable.

After playing air hockey, the pinball machines or the fruit machines you may have enough money left for the abundance for the tipping point machines. By the way I think it is appropriate that the fruit machines are called one armed bandits, as that is exactly what they are. The two-armed human version sits in the tiny kiosk where you exchange notes and large coins for lots of smaller currency.

The man never looks happy. Just sits there. Rarely moves. The first time I saw him in his change booth I actually thought it was a stuffed animal. Only when it moved did I realise there was a human being in there.

It looks as though he has spent years in solitary confinement, and it is beginning to take its toll; especially on his power of speech which seems to be seriously diminished. Grunts rather than any actual words. Not sure being indoors in dimmed light helps either. Pale faced and almost silent. He looks over his arcade and must not be disturbed. Just feed him with coins. I am not even sure if he ever gets out. Not seen daylight for years or had a good meal.

Now those tipping point machines. You have probably seen them. They have trays of pennies loaded on to shelves and all looking if they are just about to fall off. By dropping your own pennies at the right time, you can nudge some of them off the trays and back into your hands. It may sound tedious. It is not. In fact, it is mesmerising and addictive. I have lost count of the number of hours this summer I have already been caught up in this. It is also a good spectator sport as people tend to gather round as the tension and excitement rises. The sound of all those pennies dropping into your hands is as much the soundtrack of Seahouses as the seagulls.

Staying inside does damage your eyesight. It is so dark that stepping back out into the real world is like being dazzled by a very powerful light or torch. You have been inside so long tipping pennies and failing to grab any prizes that you have to get accustomed to daylight all over again. There are some of those mini rides on the pavement, little cars and aeroplanes, which amusingly have the sign 'for children only'—good thing we know that, otherwise who knows what might happen.

Just down the road from the arcade is a quite wonderful gift shop. Chaotic barely describes it. It seems to have been there before the Romans and it never closes. There is always a vast array of buckets, spades and balls outside on the pavement. They stack up to the size of a tower block and stretch into the distance. But just wait until you go inside.

It is less like a shop and more like a maze. I am sure there are people who entered in 1928 and have never found their way out. It is that complicated. You can see what you want but getting there is a bit tricky. To get to the kites or the souvenir calendars is a tortuous circuit with more twists and turns than a Blackpool rollercoaster. Added hazards are everything from plastic cricket bats and windshields dangling from the ceiling to assorted toys, calendars, postcards, and other oddities lining the floor and putting space a real premium. I have seen staff half-heatedly filling the shelves by opening boxes and randomly scattering the contents everywhere.

Every time I go in, which strangely is rather a lot, there are hoards of other people in and no system. One-way or traffic lights would be useful. You often see something you might think could be handy but end up in the place you started before getting anywhere near it. Today I bought a beach ball. Will never use it but it almost seems an insult to buy nothing and leave. The staff seem to enjoy the chaos of it all. If you find your way to the till from the maze you are rewarded by paying for something you didn't want. If you ask for something they just say vaguely "*it is over there*" as though that is accurate enough. The words needle and haystack come to mind. One consolation is the fact they must get the same questions every day.

"Where do I find the kites?"

"How much are your buckets and spades?"

"Can I get to the Farne Islands from here?"

"Do you have any tea towels with Puffins on?"

"Do you ever close?"

"My friend came in three weeks ago. Have you seen him?"

"The Milk Bar across the road sells 66's. What are they?"

"Can I have Monkey Blood with that?"

Just round the corner from the gift shop is a fishing museum cleverly disguised as a public house.

You make think you have actually boarded a pirate ship as you navigate a narrow entrance and a couple of steps that bring you to an Aladdin's cave of the deep. Oars, lobster pots, diving helmets, lamps, crates, and other assorted nautical artifacts hang from the ceiling and adorn the walls. A narrow window at one end gives a tantalising glimpse of the harbour and the distant Farne Islands. You can almost smell the seaweed and feed the seagulls. It is as though Grace Darling herself is serving behind the bar, engaging one and all with tales of daring rescues as she pulls the pints and dishes out the peanuts and crisps. The crisps are in packets with little blue packets of salt.

It really is unique and a place where the locals seem to mingle happily with the visitors in flip flops, clutching tea towels of Puffins and asking more silly questions.

"Can you get to the Farne Islands from here?"

"Are Craster kippers from Craster?"

"Why is Seahouses the only place around here without a castle?"

"What are lobster pots for?"

"Do monks still come here for a lock-in.?"

I do have sympathy with them. To be fair this is a place I don't often have the pleasure. I like it too much and could spend all night and then how would I get back to base. It is a rare treat but as they say absence makes the heart grow fonder.

To be fair the fishing theme is only right. The place used to be a welcoming watering hole for the many trawlermen visiting from other ports. It is now popular with the local fishing fleet. It casts a watchful eye over the harbour.

It is just another little place, that makes Seahouses so quirky. As is the name of the place. It suggests it is exactly what it is. Historians tell us Seahouses was originally named Sunderland, then North Sunderland to distinguish it from the town with a football team nowhere as good as Newcastle. This was a mile or so inland from the sea.

A purpose-built fishing community which originally comprised small cottages or sea houses was later constructed nearer the North Sea and took its own identity as Seahouses.

The two still sit side by side in harmony. Or at least I think so but then I don't live here in the long dark days of winter. Maybe under the cover of darkness it becomes like West Side story with and the Sharks and the Jets taking over the streets or even rival ice-cream men settling old scores. Moustache man hiding in the alley ways.

Mayhem and mass brawls. Territory and turf wars. There is going to be a rumble. Who knows what happens under the cover of darkness as the dark winter skies replace the innocent light days of summer. Probably a good job I am not sticking around. The only blood I know is Monkey Blood. I really don't want to see the real thing spilling across Seahouses and flowing into North Sunderland.

Alongside the pub, milk bar, gift shop and amusement arcade, the rest of the main street, and only street, in Seahouses has a few shops, bakery and newsagents. There is only one way in and one way out. Everyone, locals and tourists, seem on the surface to mingle well together; in a way they need each other. It is nearly always bustling and busy but rarely reaching overspill.

The harbour slopes away just down from the centre and there is always an interesting mix of fishing boats and assorted vessels to easily pass the time away. There is always plenty going on. Crabs and fish being landed, fishermen enjoying the company of other fisher folk, no doubt comparing catches and nodding about the best spots to fish. There is always lots of laughter, loud talk and seemingly endless coiling of ropes and scrubbing of decks. It is real life at a working seaside town. These guys are here all the year round, up in the early hours and battling against the waves to bring home the goods and pay their wages. Not as tough as being an ice cream man I hear you mock. Yes, I know I have an easy life. But I do work long hours and it is fairly back breaking. Okay, you can put the violins down now. I am not really after sympathy. It is my choice to be here, and I love it.

The harbour was originally a small wooden jetty between two natural rock promontories before it developed into the bustling place we see today. It is always worth a visit as there is always plenty going on. The rows of sheds offering Farne Island trips, boats leaving for the islands, other boats on dry land for repair, people just ambling along eating fish and chips and gazing out into the vastness of the North Sea. Next stop Norway.

To Boldy Not To Go

Yet another sunny day. I feel like an emergency service. People flagging me down again. Well let's hope so.

There are rules in the ice cream world—some I have already touched on. Like don't worry where your rivals go. You can always get there first, have some tricks up your sleeve or simply chase them around.

But never go where others in your team boldly go. There are boundaries. A certain camaraderie. For instance, I would never dream of touring the villages where *"you bugger but I sold some pop"* goes. It is his manor, his customers, his living. To do that would be the ultimate cardinal sin and you would soon be cast out like a broken cone. Useless and unwanted. A cone of shame would hang round your neck and you would probably be put in the stocks, covered in Monkey Blood and catapulted with chocolate flakes. It is that serious. Don't go there.

I have established Beadnell harbour as my spot and my spot alone. All trespassers will be prosecuted. Keep out. Keep away. The sailing club, the nomadic beach tribes, dog walkers and the paddlers are all my punters. I have cornered the market. Worked hard, well not all the time, to get here. Don't even think about it.

Same with the army of caravanners. The end of day site tours are my battlegrounds. I have conquered them with chocolate and no man should take away. Never mind standing on the first step—I have climbed the whole staircase. I am staying here.

All this came to mind on this sunny day and thinking of other options. A trip to Bamburgh would be nice. The sight of that castle never fails to amaze and inspire. It is perched on top of the village like some giant windshield protecting the village from everything the wild and sometimes stormy North Sea can throw at it. It also like a comfort blanket. When you see it, you just feel safe. No one is going to get past that. It really is a rock.

I see it again as my van ambles along and into the tiny postcard like hamlet. It also provides the backdrop to what must surely be the most stunning cricket ground around. You can forget about Lords, Trent Bridge, or the Oval, this has to be the best. The castle looks down on it, like some giant sight screen ensuring the action is not interrupted. The players look like some kind of collection of David's in the shadow of Goliath.

Watching a game of cricket here is just paradise. Playing, although I am no good with bat or ball, must be even better. Imagine running in from the castle end. You must feel you have an almighty strength behind you. The ball must travel even faster or taken even a more wicked spin. History is on your side.

I say this out of jealously as there alongside the field and just below the fortress is my trusted colleague, Jimmy. With his white hair and pristine white coat, he would not be out of place mixing cocktails at the Ritz or serving very expensive tiny cups of coffee to those who can afford to sit in St Mark's Square, Venice.

His spot here in Bamburgh just seems the perfect fit. There is certain serenity to it all. The pace of life just seems that little bit slower. People just really enjoy being here. It is unique even when there is no cricket being played. When there is, the queues to his van seem to stretch that little bit longer, but no one is in a rush. The Bamburgh button has been pushed and you are almost in a different time zone. It is quintessential England. An ice cream, cricket and a castle and all seems well with the world.

Jimmy's coat is so white I often think he could be mistaken for an umpire and imagine him waving his hand to signal a boundary, as he simultaneously serves a 99. It could even be 99 not out. Jimmy was born to be here.

He is also one of the quietest people I have ever met. His hushed tones are so hushed, you feel you're in the presence of greatness. Every word is carefully calculated before being delivered. You have to listen. It would be rude not to. Every word comes with wisdom.

To get there before him and park your van in his spot would be the ultimate insult. He may be quiet but don't be surprised if you wake up in bed tomorrow with a horse's head next to you. He is the main man. El supremo, Number One, Van the Man, The Conefather. You would only mess with him once.

As I drive past him, he gives a knowing nod. Nice to see you but keep on driving. And I normally do. It is just great to see Bamburgh now and again in all its glory. A lovely village green cornered in by a triangle of roads and the small number of general stores, coffee shops, pubs and cottages lying neatly behind newly mown grassy slopes. It is idyllic. Come and see it for yourself.

At the top end lies the magnificent St Aiden's church. Not magnificent in terms of size or architecture but simply in setting. It has one eye on the castle and the other roving across the sea to the faraway Farnes. No wonder it is a popular place for births, deaths and marriages. If this was my final resting place, I would certainly have a tomb with a view.

It is a lovely spot. I am not a hugely religious person. In that area my only elevated status comes from being a member of the choir at the local Sunday School when I was still in shorts. I have still got a specially inscribed hymn book as evidence that I was actually there.

Nowadays my singing, and I use that term rather loosely, is restricted to the bath or when I am alone in the van with only the radio for company. I do draw a line at joining in with 'Save Your Kisses For Me' though. I am probably tone deaf as well which probably helps when Brotherhood of Man are in full voice. Some unkind people have even suggested it also helps when listening to Dylan. Yes, he is not the best singer in the world but that is not really the point. Just listen to the words. Shakespeare or Bob? It is a close contest.

At school, I did try and play the violin, but

my teacher finally gave up when I said the first two notes at the beginning of the national anthem, God Save the Queen, were different. Go on, I can hear you humming it now. Hope you are standing up. They are actually the same notes. Oh dear.

But here at St Aidan's, especially when you are alone and the sun is beginning to set, there is definitely something spiritual going on. Or maybe it is just a nice place to be.

Certainly, St Aidan thought that when King Oswald of Northumbria brought him back to Bamburgh from Iona in about 625AD, probably the last time Newcastle United won a trophy, to establish Christianity in the newly United Kingdom of Northumbria. He died here and there is a nice shrine inside the church dedicated to his memory as the Apostle of Northumbria. The beam he was leaning against when he gave his last breath is said to be still here in the church. I do find that a bit spooky.

Originally a wooden structure the church here today dates back to the end of the 12th century and still attracts thousands of pilgrims and visitors every year. The only difference now is fortunately many of them arrive for ice creams from Seahouses' finest, the beaches and the castles and nothing deeper.

Before I leave Bamburgh there is still time for a little trip along the Wynding. As the name implies this is a lovely little winding road that surfs the top of the beach and comes to end at Bamburgh golf course, where you have to circle round near the first tee and come back.

It is very narrow with barely enough space for two cars, never mind ice cream vans, to pass. There are also some very nice and very big houses along the way. Near the end there is scattering of smaller but superbly positioned cottages with great sea views. Looking from the windows you must feel as you could almost touch the Puffins on the Farne Islands.

There is also a white stag painted on the rocks just below the road. It has been there for years. I am not sure if anyone knows the real history. There are many stories. One legend says it marks the escape of a white deer which jumped into the sea having run from a hunt. Another says it was painted by Italian prisoners-of-war during World War Two and a third that it was painted by a local artist in the early 1900s. I reckon it could be a mischievous prank left over from a boisterous stag party.

The golf course, here I go again, is spectacular. As you tee off from the seventeenth I think, I could be wrong, the fairway is wrapped with the castle in the background. Who cares if you slice your drive into the rough and take three putts to finish, it is not a bad hole. But I am not a golfer and go by what I have been told.

There are other courses scattered along the coast. Seahouses is much shorter than Bamburgh and one best suited to my limited abilities. Then there is Dunstanburgh Castle Golf Club which has a very testing par three over a narrow ravine onto a small green with the ruins of the fortress just behind. I have said it before. But this is also spectacular.

Bamburgh always feels as though it is looking down on its near neighbours of Seahouses and Beadnell. But in a rather nice sort of comfortable way. Nothing nasty or condescending. It just knows it stands for that bit of extra quality. You almost have to talk in hushed tones as you wander around. There should be a sign at the entrances saying "*Welcome to Bamburgh. Do Not Disturb.*"

There are some really big houses here and some of them are second homes. Just makes you think how big their homes are back in Newcastle or wherever. It is all gentile and sometimes there is really no need to talk. Just breathing in the sights of the castle, the cricket ground or going for a walk on the magnificent beach is enough. But when leaving, remember to take all your litter back to Beadnell or Seahouses. No silly hats, fish and chip shops or amusement arcades here, thank you very much. We are above all that.

Anyhow that is Bamburgh for me for today. It is Jimmy's patch and that is how it should be. They are perfectly matched. Almost made for each other. Sad to leave it behind but Beadnell is my real ice cream home. The spiritual resting place for many 99's, 66's and nougat wafers. Bye bye Bamburgh. Hope my presence was not too disturbing.

***

Beadnell, in contrast to its more refined neighbour, is more flip-flops and tee-shirts than the pristine white coats and tranquility of Bamburgh. Just a harmless place by the sea with no hidden agenda. What you see is what you get.

Beadnell has a kind of understated informality. It just seems to get along quite nicely. There is a sense of innocent pleasure. The beach, the harbour, the lime kilns, the neat well-kept little houses, the orderly caravan sites, and the good old fresh sea air with nothing to interrupt it. People like the innocence of Beadnell. I hope it never changes.

Seahouses is the sandwich filling between Bamburgh and Beadnell. As noted before not quite Blackpool but the only place around for fish and chips, kites, novelty gifts and amusements. Unrefined compared to Bamburgh and more in your face than Beadnell. Somehow the chemistry works and all three combine to give the real seaside experience for all. They live comfortably side by side and if truth be known, they couldn't really do without each other. It really is a case of opposites attracting. I also like the fact there is a stretch of open road between all the villages, giving you a chance for some space and keeping the separate entities apart. Please keep it his way. They all have their own unique character and would never feel comfortable being joined up.

I do have a soft spot for Beadnell. It is basically my childhood. It is where we were hugely fortunate to have our summer holidays every year and strangely reminds me of waiting outside the tiny shop near the camp site or the bus to arrive and drop off the Football Pinks on a Saturday. What? I hear you say. They are the special edition of the local Newcastle newspaper giving a move-by-move account of how the football team had got on. Other regional papers may have their own equivalent. All goals in the report, which is a kick-by-kick account of the match, are highlighted in bold and there is also a full list of all results and tables. It was always my favourite read of the week with the anticipation and suspense only increasing as arrival time got nearer.

Enough of that. I am just arriving in Beadnell. It is barely four miles from Bamburgh for those that can't remember.

Getting here from Bamburgh is a glorious drive. The road to Seahouses ambles along with occasional glimpses of the sea and those islands to one side and rolling countryside with the Cheviot Hills in the distance on the other. It's a heady mix of sheep and seagulls.

Then you enter the houses by the sea, with the wonderful gift shop to your left and our van loading bay just across the road from the ice cream factory. Swing past the roundabout, the amusement arcade, a couple of fish and chip shops and then back on the open road to Beadnell. The golf course is on your left, then a farm, rolling grasslands backing onto the sea, a campsite and then the village itself.

My base is a small caravan tucked away on a small site just behind the grandly named Beadnell Hall Hotel. And it certainly must have been grand in its day but maybe not so much today.

Once upon a time this grand old building was the hallmark of fine dining and silver service. It was the place for the wealthy and even wealthier. Tennis courts outside and inside, plenty of large rooms and plenty of space. Halfway up the winding staircase is a glass case with a stuffed lion, or is a bear or some other animal? No, I am not making this up. Not entirely sure how it got there or why it is there. It must have shocked countless guests as they made their way up to their rooms after some fine feasting and goblets of wine.

"Bloody hell, don't look now but there is a lion on the stairs!"

"Oh come on dear, I think you've had a little bit too much to drink. Come on, I think you need to lie down. Things will be a lot clearer in the morning."

"My God, it's still there. I think I might skip breakfast today."

Even today the grand old building still does have that aura about it. A grand entrance, large wooden doors, richly carpeted rooms and high ceilings. It certainly is a grand place. You can imagine horse drawn carriages lining up outside with waiting uniformed gentlemen ready to escort the fancily dressed occupants into the huge halls and ready for the banquet. You can almost hear the orchestra playing.

As for that stuffed animal, I don't see it that often as I class myself as a tradesman and use the back door to nip into the small but very friendly public bar where I can mix with other locals. Their tales of the past, not to say their alcohol consumption, can be quite frightening. But I think I have been accepted, as the jovial man behind bar always gives me a friendly greeting as I enter. I don't go every night I hasten to add just in case you were thinking I have a problem. It is a fairly rare occurrence as I am here to save money and not splash it away all the time on amusement arcades and beer parlours.

Next door is the eerie Beadnell House Hotel. I say that because it always looks empty. It is the kind of place you would expect the Boo Radleys to live and Jem and Scout to come knocking on his door. I think I have even seen Atticus Finch walk by several times. It really is To Kill a Mockingbird territory. It has huge windows which afford a view into what seems to be, very large and very empty rooms. Who really knows what goes on behind closed doors? I guess it is all very innocent. Just a nice place to stay and eat. But I do have visions of no one saying a word. It must be really quiet, where silence, reading great works of literature and maybe the soft sound of classical music in the background is the order of the day.

I say this as I have rarely ventured inside. No, I have never ventured inside. I am almost too scared to see what I might find. Maybe skeletons of guests past, meals left uneaten, beds unmade and shredded curtains rustling in the wind. It was once an aged persons dwelling and maybe the ghosts of the past still linger.

But I am told there are people in there. They seem to be well catered for. Hearty and healthy meals, raising a glass or two of the most expensive red wine round, burning embers on the fireplace and then sleeping undisturbed in their sumptuous and comfortable beds.

Although there is a large, round, well gravelled path which takes you to the entrance and out to the exit, there never seems to be anyone actually using it. No one on foot, no one in a car. Not entirely sure how people access the interior. All very weird and all adding to the mystical and haunted look of the old place.

***

Today I am back in my usual spot. Parked within inches of the beach at Beadnell harbour. It is an ice cream trap as I can capture almost everyone. Not literally of course. That would put punters off. No, people have to walk past me to get to the sand or along to the harbour or even those who are launching their sailing dinghies. I am in such a good mood I have even positioned the plastic bottle of Monkey Blood in full view. Everyone can have some today if they want. But hopefully it will run out quickly and I have no intention of refilling it. First come first served as they say. Book early to avoid disappointment.

That mood has not always lasted though. Please forgive me but I have sinned. On the odd occasion I have been so sick of the sight of Monkey Blood I have actually poured the contents onto the sand and covered it over.

Then when the next unsuspecting young boy or girl comes along, I say if you run on the spot, you can get your next ice cream for free. And they do. Up and down on the sand until it all sticks to their feet as the ghastly red fluid rises to the surface.

Even when you put this misdemeanor together with chasing moustached man, getting Captain Fantastic a personal call for his bar meal and giving away chocolate flakes, I am sure I will not be pulled in for questioning by the police. It is the 1970s. You have to make your own fun. Just don't tell the boss. He might tell "*you bugger I sold some pop*" man and word will quickly spread that I am not to be trusted. I may be breaking some unwritten rules of the ice cream world. I would be cast out from the brotherhood of ice cream, never to hold a cone again and never welcome back. I could end up with my old van covered in Monkey Blood, left to rust and the chimes still playing.

This silly habit of pouring Monkey Blood on the sand, is probably just revenge for being asked "what is a 66" so many times. It is not serious. I just feel better afterwards. After cones comes counseling. The sand dance seems to work. It does make me smile if no one else.

Right, van parked, engine off. Another notable triumph as I actually made it here on the harbour without breaking down. That is the van not me. Another day in paradise.

It is late morning. A great time of the day. The van is loaded and parked. The radio is on and the sun is shining. This is the calm before the storm. Not a great deal of demand for ice cream at the moment. I do pick up the odd person dropping by for a couple of cans of pop to go with their picnic lunch on the beach. They will need something to wash away the sand from the sandwiches. Or maybe a couple of dog walkers looking to cool down with a cone after a strenuous walk.

The soft drink cans aren't even stored in a cool place. They are perched near the back window. If I am feeling creative, I sometime stock an assortment next to serving hatch just to entice a few more sales. But I am not really that bothered. I am here to sell ice cream.

Having sporadic sales can be annoying. You are up one minute, down the next. Reading the book and then putting it down. It is tempting to put a closed sign on the side. *'Go away, can't you see I am relaxing'*—I have had a hard morning already. Breakfast, cleaning and loading the van, general chit chat with the rest of the gang before they set out on their travels and the usual banter about sales of pop and which customer annoyed you the most yesterday. I always say it is the guy in the peaked sailor's cap who thinks he has just successfully navigated his way round Cape Horn and wants to quibble about the price of his ice cream.

We also discuss the merits of the menu at

our morning briefings. I argue against having 66's included. It just gets boring with the same questions every day. Can't we just have 99's on offer and leave it at that. It all gets a bit confusing not to say tedious as I am the same question time after time. The boss man, Seahouses born and bred, has little time for small talk. *"Just carry on. There will be no changes."*

To be fair, as I have said, he is very trusting. He gives me loose change every morning or a floater as it is known in the retail world. This is put on the wooden tray which laughingly is my cash register. It does have different sections for different coins and notes but that is at far as it goes. It sits the far side of the fridges and out of reach prying eyes or careless hands.

By the end of the day there can be a tidy sum there. I am not joking when I say it is constantly at the higher end of three figures. I count it out and hand it over. There are no receipts, no accounts, just good old-fashioned trust. I suspect he does know roughly how much there should be and I know he turns a blind eye if I take out the odd few coins or a note to supplement my fish and chips supper that night. Occasionally it does pay for a couple of pints of Newcastle Exhibition or McEwans Best Scotch.

The day's takings are never really discussed. They are just met with a kindly nod and a "*well done son, see you tomorrow.*" Occasionally, the boss does turn up unexpectedly. Sometimes he camouflages himself into the queue or stands at a distance. Either way you never know if you are being watched. That is his cunning plan. Keeps you on your toes. Just his way of making sure you are out and about selling and not off on a day trip to Edinburgh. He has occasionally surprised me by opening the driver's door and leaping into the van without warning. Now that is quite scary. He doesn't hang around. Just a quick check and a cheery nod and he is on his way. Suppose it keeps me on my toes and it always good to know he is interested. To date, and there is still a long summer to go, he has not caught me sleeping, reading or selling anything else other than ice cream or soft drinks. Maybe cigarettes and cold beer would go down well but that is not what we do.

This is the safest part of the day. You have just loaded up, set off and settled in your favourite spot. Little chance of the boss being around. He wants to be here when the action starts and the ice creams are being churned out the churns quicker than you can say "*what is a 66, an upside down 99?*"

No this is my time. Get the radio on and chill. I love the radio. I have already told you I am not a scientist and I really have no idea how it works. How someone can be talking to me from Lords or the Oval, commentating on a football match or even telling me what the weather is going to be like today. I am always amazed. It has to be the greatest invention in the world. A great companion. Informs, educates and entertains. Reliable and always there when you want it. Never argues, goes in the huff or lets you down.

Music, sport and news with the occasional comedy or documentary. It brings us such classics as 'Desert Island Discs'—'I'm Sorry I Haven't a Clue' and the everlasting 'Sports Report' every Saturday.

The theme music for Sports Report comes with the taste of Bovril and the sound of rattles. The headlines are tantalising. *Liverpool score four, Burnley get a last-minute penalty and still no win for bottom of the table Stoke City.* The music fades and makes way for the rhythmic poetry of the results. The change in inflection tells you immediately if your team has won, lost or drawn. *Arsenal 1 Newcastle,* wait for it the voice has stayed the same, we have got a draw. Yes, *Newcastle 1.* Still waiting for "East Fife four Forfar five" to come through one day.

It is magical. It was not so long ago that we would rush back to the car after a game at St James' Park and Dad would turn the radio on just in time for the music to begin. I still love it. Sports Report has been going since 1948. Or thereabouts. Long may it continue. Maybe the theme tune, 'Out of the Blue' by Herbert Bath if you are interested, could be our National Anthem. It is that important.

Bryon Butler, the former BBC football correspondent, once said about the programme: *"Britain was still frayed and shaken by a war it had won and ration books still mattered more than any written by Shakespeare, but sport helped provide the promise of a better tomorrow in one heady and irresistible package. Queues wrapped themselves around football and cricket grounds like endless woolen scarves. People wanted excitement and sport answered the call."*

Desert Island Discs is another good one. Haven't we all secretly chosen our castaway music and luxury? Bit of Bob Dylan for a start and a radio would be a must. Not sure of that is allowed though. The radio that it is, not Robert Zimmerman.

Digressing again, time for the first customer of the day. Off we go again. Do you want Monkey Blood with that?

The Blood Of A Monkey

Now is the time to come clean. Or in this case a bit messy. What exactly is Monkey Blood and why is it called that.

First off, in my case, it is a red strawberry or raspberry flavoured liquid that is barely contained in a plastic bottle. A quick squeeze and it comes gushing out. It always seems out of control. No matter how much or how little pressure you apply, it always comes out faster than you expect. The aim is to add it to the top of the ice cream you have just served. In a way, it is bit like being a cocktail waiter and your chance to show off your deft skills as you swirl your hand round in an effortless manner. Out it comes to send artistic circles round the ice cream...

It is even better if you just keep talking, don't break stride or pause for breath. It is an artist at work. It may look easy, but it isn't. It takes a certain skill, certain patience and a certain eye for detail. The end product is a work of art. You could photograph it, frame it and sign it. It would not look out of a place in a gallery, lounge wall or hallway. It might be even worth a few bob in years to come.

Imagine people staring at it and musing on the meaning.

"Look at the vivid colours. The contrast between the red and white. It is commentary on life itself. The differences in society and how we all come together for the good of the human spirit."

"Oh yes, I see what you mean. The cone is the mountain we are all climbing and the red shows the diversions in the way. Very clever. So simple, so moving. I have always admired his work."

"There is always something different every time you look at it. And the title Monkey Blood, well, that says it all. How we have evolved from animals, the spilling of blood over the centuries, war and peace and all that."

Okay, I might be getting carried away just a

little. The real truth is the fact it is a horrible, gooey sticky mess that somehow ends up more over your hands and trousers that it does on the ice cream. It is supposed to have a raspberry or strawberry flavour. Don't ask me. It just looks awful and probably tastes awful and God knows what it does for your digestive system and internal organs. Probably not something the good doctor would prescribe for a healthy life. But that literally all seems to go out the window when it comes to such a summer delicacy.

People on holiday are generally carefree and careless. All rules are to be broken. "*Who cares what it is. Just give me some more. Summer won't be summer without a bit of Monkey Blood. Come on, pour it all over, the more the better. We are here to have fun. Normality can wait for a while.*"

And what gets me is, no one ever queries why it is called Monkey Blood. Yes, loads of questions about 66's, how do you get to the Farne Islands, why to Puffins look like parrots and is Northumberland in Scotland, but nothing, absolutely nothing about this red liquid.

You would think if someone offered you Monkey Blood at least you would have the decency to hesitate and question before sealing the deal. But no. It is always,

"Do you want Monkey Blood with that?"

"Oh yes please."

It is never.

"I beg your pardon. What did you just say? Am I hearing you right? Did you just offer be the blood of a monkey?"

"That is disgusting. Have you just clashed with a chimp or angered an ape? All I wanted was a vanilla ice cream. I wasn't expecting the added wildlife. Where is the deceased animal or has it just cut itself accidentally and you thought that would taste nice? You must be mad. I am taking my custom elsewhere. But I will be reporting you to the RSPCA first."

"Monkey Blood indeed. You haven't heard the last of it."

"Don't go near this guy. He has just killed an animal. There is blood everywhere. He even wants to put it on your ice cream. He should be locked up. It is not an ice cream van. It is a crime scene. I am calling the police."

You could just as well have said: *"Nice day again"* for all the affect it has. No one ever batters an eyelid. Strange, very strange.

There again I am complicit to all this. I have never questioned the meaning of Monkey Blood myself. It is something I have always known, something I have grown up with. To me, ice cream always came with Monkey Blood. Why wouldn't it after all. Makes sense doesn't it. It's like bread and butter, fish and chips, some things just go together. Morecambe and Wise, horse and carriage, salt and vinegar.

But this is no laughing matter. Especially if you have to serve it every day. No matter how often you wash your hands the distinctive glue-like fluid never rubs off. It gets everywhere and is very stubborn when it comes to removal.

No problem if you splash it all round one

cone and hand it over to the waiting punters. It is a problem if there is no time between servings and person after person all want the same offering. Your hands end up bloodied and red, like some scene from a horror movie. Again, no one in the queue queries this.

"Have you just sliced your hand with a bread knife?"

"Should I call an ambulance?"

"Looks nasty. Are you sure you should be working? I would get that seen to if I were you."

"Hope the other guy is OK."

Nothing. It is acceptable that ice cream men and women in Northumberland look as though they also have part time work in the nearest abattoir. I still have no idea why strawberry or raspberry sauce in an ice cream topping form, is referred to as Monkey Blood.

I did think I hit the jackpot when I located this comment from some research

"Having been in the ice cream business for about thirty years I can say with the greatest

confidence" ......yes go on...... *"I don't have a clue where the name originated from. I used to use four or five gallons a week of the stuff."*

So, there you are. Utterly clueless. It is probably just a reference used in this part of the world and other northern outposts. If you used it in sprawling inner city London, you might get driven out of town by the local hoodlums. Up here on the historic Northumberland coast it seems like some kind of everyday greeting. You would be rude not to pose the question. Might look a bit unfriendly. Don't want to upset anybody.

I feel I have to stock it and make it available. It 'rubber stamps' your authority around here as a bona fide ice cream man. It is a badge of honour, your passport to the ice cream underworld. Maybe, there is some kind of ceremony that is not spoken about but might be as old as the castles.

"Come on son. Time to make a man out of you. An ice cream man. I put my finger into this here Monkey Blood and dab it on your

forehead. Your time has come. You will never walk a cone. Hold your head up high. Now run off into the North Sea and wash it away to the spirits in the sky. They will look after you. Never again will be you angry when asked what a 66 is. You have joined the ancient brotherhood. You will sell vanilla; you will sell some pop and all your wafers will be nougat."

Okay, farfetched, but the most plausible explanation I can come up with. Do you have any better ones? No. I didn't think so.

As already mentioned, I may have bended the secret code on many occasions. Pretending I don't have any on board is possibly poor behaviour, alongside pouring it on the sand and encouraging people to dance. Monkey Blood may have some pagan qualities, even today. It is not to be messed with even though it certainly messes with you.

Strangely it is never mentioned in my morning catchups with the rest of the gang. No one ever queries how much Monkey Blood you used yesterday. Even saying the name might bring bad luck. The Macbeth of the ice cream world. I can't even remember ever refilling the plastic bottle. Miraculously it never seems to empty.

Even though I may have hidden it or thrown it way, it is still there every morning when I pick up the van. Now that is spooky. It is never spoken about. Nougat wafers and 99's are safer territory. Talk about the weather, what you did last night, the last time Newcastle United won a game. Anything but that. Break a leg.

I am not even sure where it is stored. There must be a vat or a very large tank lying around somewhere where you go and dip your bottles like some summer ritual. Bit like Morris Dancing, often done but never talked about or questioned.

Come to think of I have never actually refilled my Monkey Blood bottle. Mysteriously someone has always done it for me and it just reappears replenished and ready to go. It is as though I am not allowed to see the supply or uncover the secrets of the storage. It could be sealed in some kind of chamber of horrors which you are not allowed to enter until you have been an ice cream man for at least ten years.

For the moment it all remains a mystery and as long as it disappears as quickly as possible then I happy not to resolve it. Sometimes it is just wise not to venture where you don't need to go. Leave it all in the dark and don't ask too many questions. I probably don't want to hear the answers.

In Search Of The Holy Ice Cream

Today I am taking a huge decision. No more Beadnell or Bamburgh or even a quick trip back to Craster. No, I am going on a pilgrimage and following the footsteps of those barefoot monks from hundreds of years ago. I am off to Holy Island, the cradle of Christianity on a pint-sized tidal island that is cut off from the rest of the world twice a day. It is a faraway land miles away from Seahouses, almost a day trip in itself. A faraway land.

The Anglo-Saxon name of the island is Lindisfarne, a name adopted by one of Newcastle's finest bands who gave us Fog on the Tyne. It wouldn't have been as quite as catchy to call themselves Holy Island I suppose.

"Please welcome on stage Holy Island" would be more like a geography field trip than a concert. But I guess Lindisfarne the band have

done enough to give this tiny island some twenty miles up the coast from Seahouses a bit of a modern-day comeback.

Fog on the Tyne has virtually been adopted as the national anthem for Newcastle. The chorus of the *Fog on the Tyne is all mine* makes sense but not sure about...

Could a copper catch a crooked coffin maker
Could a copper comprehend
That a crooked coffin maker is just an undertaker who
Undertakes to be a friend
But then again, these following words probably paint a better North East picture
Tell the truth tomorrow
Today will take its time to
Tell you what tonight might bring
Presently we'll have a pint or two together
Everybody do their thing

Lindisfarne is Christmas in Newcastle. No festivities are complete until you have heard

Meet Me On The Corner, Clear White Light and Lady Eleanor belted out in sing-along mode at the town's City Hall. The band are as much part of Tyneside as the Tyne Bridge.

Holy Island still remains a place of great peace and tranquility, dating back to about 650AD when the Irish monk Aidan arrived here from Iona on the west coast of Scotland, and he probably got here quicker than my trip today in this old van of mine.

He was joined in the 670s by another monk named Cuthbert who quickly sealed the island's reputation as the cradle of Christianity. He was made a Bishop in 685AD and was one of the all-time religious greats as a pastor and a healer. I am sure there were also a few more monks wandering around as there was a monastery.

Interestingly, the monastic way of life on Holy Island was even too noisy for Cuthbert and he later became a bit of a recluse and lived alone on island just offshore, now called St Cuthbert's Isle, before moving further away across the sea to the remote island of Inner Farne. Not sure what he would have made of Seahouses on a busy summer day or Beadnell when the beach is bustling.

I just love the thought of him sneaking his way round the gift shop and coming away with a kite to take back to Holy Island and show off to his mates.

The remains of the Priory are still pretty impressive, especially the Rainbow Arch which has somehow survived despite the central tower above it collapsing more than 200 years ago.

Just up from the Priory is the glorious Lindisfarne Castle. It is a much smaller version of its bigger brother down the road at Bamburgh, but still very impressive. It looks as though it has been stuck on top of a craggy outcrop with a bit of glue and could fall off at any minute.

Compared to the Priory, the castle has led a bit of a charmed life. Originally home to a garrison of soldiers from nearby Berwick, it was never really under threat. Being posted there was a bit of a cushy number with just regular gun practice to keep you entertained. Who knows what else they got up to. Probably not a lot as there was just seagulls, seals and other assorted wildlife for company.

By 1901, with the help of renowned architect Edwin Lutyen, the castle was converted into a holiday home and is now in the hands of the National Trust. It is a great place to visit with the steep walk to the entrance enticing and exhilarating, leading you into a myriad of small rooms and alcoves and great sea views.

In contrast, the Priory was vandalised by marauding Vikings and the monks had to get out and did not come back for another four hundred years.

Today, the island has probably less than 200 residents, a couple of pubs, at least one hotel, the usual array of gift shops and tearooms, along with thousands of visitors.

The only way to get across is by driving

across the causeway. It was put together sometime in the 1950s. For the previous 1,300 years the Pilgrims Way footpath, marked with a line of upright poles, was the only access to the island.

Despite the myriad of notices displaying the times when you can cross, there are still some drivers, who at the first sign of the sea covering bits of the thin strip of concrete, decide it is time to nip across and risk it. Do they not know tide waits for no man, can't they read or are they just incredibly stupid? Possibly a lethal cocktail of all three. It is really annoying when they end up having to abandon their vehicle barely halfway across and have to leg it up steps to a wooden shelter and wait for rescue. By that time, their car will hopefully be submerged.

Every year there is a trail of travellers getting caught out through their own mindless actions. They should all be made to pay for the cost of recovery. There are the usual calls for better warning signs or barriers but in my view the present system is thoroughly sensible and straightforward.

There is even talk about building a bridge to the island. This would just remove all the mystery and unique quality of such a special place. Being cut off and living by the rhythms of the tide must be a great way to live. The monks had no problem. Walking barefoot across the sand was good enough for them.

So Holy Island is my very own pilgrimage today. I haven't even told the boss. Not sure I am allowed to venture so far away from my natural habitat. It is about twenty miles away but getting there in the ice cream van could be a bit of marathon. Not even sure I have enough petrol to make it all the way there and back.

My mind is made up. If men can get to the moon I can get to Holy Island. But I am not sure if I will be landing on a sea of tranquility, as a rogue ice cream van may not be welcomed. And it's not as though I will not be noticed—a vintage van in garish yellow and blue colours is hard to miss.

I do not mention my itinerary to colleagues. I am sure *"you bugger I sold some pop"* man would be less than impressed. Venturing far away from the villages and hamlets of his local communities would never cross his mind and quite right to. So, I keep my madness to myself. I join in the usual cheery chat, have a quick cuppa and then I am on way north. Probably out of bounds and out of my way but nothing ventured nothing gained. One man and his van.

I do a feel a little nervous. For a start will the van get there, and if and when I get there will I be welcomed or chased away like a fox followed by hounds. Never mind the hounds it could simply be out of bounds. It has never been mentioned in our morning chats.

Yes, plenty of talk about pop, wafers, 66's, Bamburgh, Craster and Beadnell, but nothing about the Island of Holy. Is it somewhere I should be fearing to tread, to boldly not to go where others have not so boldly gone and maybe never come back? These thoughts have just begun to jumble up my mind and get me thinking when it comes to bright ideas this could be one that is not so illuminating. I could be entering a dark place.

I leave Seahouses, skirt through Bamburgh and head west on to the main A1. I do feel guilty and a little nervous as the grandeur of Bamburgh Castle fades from the rear-view mirror. It is almost waving at me, no longer standing guard and looking after me. It is almost saying *"well that's it mate, you are on your own now. Don't expect me to look after you. If I can't see you, I can't be there for you. Lindisfarne Castle is much smaller me and I am not sure it is on your side. From what I hear you may not get a good welcome. Anyhow, best of luck, you will probably need it."*

Anyhow, I push all this away as the journey goes without incident apart from the queues of frustrated motorists piling up behind me as I get to the main road to Scotland. Turning right and just off yards away there is a stopping point to check the tide tables. They really are easy to read with the safe crossing times clearly visible. I am in luck; it is safe to cross now until early evening. Suppose I should have checked before I set off, but the air of uncertainty adds to the adventure.

If you don't understand the tables at this first sight, there is really no excuse as there is another set of tide times at the very start of the causeway. Any idiot can read them. No need to race against the tide. When it's safe to cross could not be more explicit.

Driving across the causeway is a strange experience. There are just vast expanses of temporary dry land on both sides which the sea will later cover. You soon get on to the island; it all feels slightly surreal as you soak up the history of the place. There is a slightly monastic atmosphere, and you feel you should speak in whispers, maintain a vow of silence, eat some dry bread, take your shoes off and go for a walk.

I drive through the narrow lanes, flanked by the occasional cottage, and then down past the

Priory to the open grasslands that leads to the castle.

I am not even sure I am supposed to be here. There is a distinct feeling of being watched, I am half expecting to be stopped at any moment, questioned about my movements and then politely asked to turn around and go back. Possibly my van could be searched and heaven knows how I would explain the bottle of Monkey Blood. I would be seen as a pagan. But none of this, as I safely navigate to a nice little spot next to a gravel path with cars that seem to have been thrown together rather than actually parked.

I don't even dare turn my little radio on. Not sure the pilgrims would appreciate a break in the silence. I need to fit in as well as I can. I am testing the water, don't really want to upset anyone. Well, I am here now, may as well start selling. Surprisingly, I do get a few early customers as they make their way to the castle.

I am outside my comfort zone.

"Oh yes, the castle is well worth a visit. Small but interesting. Take care on the walk to the entrance though. A bit steep."

"Do you know of any good places to grab a quick snack?"

"Yes, just go into the village. There is plenty of choice."

"Is the Priory open?"

"Yes, as far as I know it never closes."

I really do feel I am in enemy territory. All of a sudden Beadnell seems a nice cosy blanket I need to get wrapped in. After a few more sales, not many, I make the decision to be a bit of a tourist and shut up shop and have a walk around.

The first place I get to is St Aidan's Winery, the home of Lindisfarne Mead. Yes, these clever monks have their very own brewery. Well, maybe not. This was set-up long after the Dissolution of Monasteries and the Vikings combined to make a life a little difficult.

According to the publicity blurb Lindisfarne

'Mead is a unique alcoholic fortified wine manufactured here on the Holy Island of Lindisfarne from fermented white grapes, honey, herbs, the pure natural water from the island's artesian well-fortified with fine spirits.

Mead has for centuries been renowned as an "aphrodisiac" and the word Honeymoon is derived from the ancient Norwegian custom of having newly-weds drink mead for a whole moon (month) in order to increase their fertility and therefore the chances of a happy and fulfilled marriage.

World famous Lindisfarne Mead is not only the connoisseur's choice but makes a supreme drink for young and old alike whatever the season. To many it is regarded as the "nectar of the gods"'

So, there you have it. Who am I to argue? I have been here before and taken advantage of the free sample from the showroom. It certainly has a unique taste and you are unlikely to order a pint. Still, it is a great tradition and long may it continue.

I have great idea for a slogan *"Lindisfarne - Mead in Northumberland"* Next time I might drop in and pass it on as trademark idea. No time for Mead today. I am supposed to be at work.

After wandering around the small but well stocked showroom, with plenty of those free samples on offer, I am beginning to feel a bit guilty, so I wander back to the van. Miraculously it is still there and not either burned at the stake or dipped in the harbour like witches all those years ago. But you know what I have lost my enthusiasm and it is a long way back to base. I don't want to get caught out by the tide and be the only ice cream van in living memory to be marooned on the causeway.

Just think of the headlines

"99 man rings 999"

"Cornets on the Causeway"

"Ice Cream Man on Flakey Ground"

You get my drift. I think it is time cut my

losses and get out of here. It has been an interesting day but not one I am likely to repeat. Next time I will just come as an ordinary visitor, enjoy the history and not feel my every move is being watched. This urge to leave is strange, almost as though someone from above is telling me. They had the Vikings, the last thing the islanders need now is an invading army of ice cream vans. They might have to get the soldiers back in the castle and the monks back in the monastery or they could just tie you up and force feed you gallons of Lindisfarne Mead. That would teach me not to trespass.

Yes, my mind is beginning to unravel. Let's just get off. And I do, returning to Seahouses as dusk is beginning to settle in and the boss has long retired for the night. How am going to explain such meagre takings on another red-hot day is another matter. Maybe I won't have to. No, tomorrow it is back to the harbour at Beadnell and the sailing and beach dwelling fraternity. It is what I like best. It is what I know best. It is all a bit worrying that I left no time to tour the caravan sites tonight. Bit of a schoolboy error really but tomorrow is another day and I have plenty of free flakes already in stock to keep the customers satisfied.

It has been a really long day and it was just great to see my old friend Bamburgh Castle towering back into view and letting me know I am near home and on safe ground. I will leave Holy Island to the monks and Mead, the castle and the causeway. Just nice to be going back to Beadnell. I feel like a retreating army back from enemy lines. No more tempting defeat when victory was secure back on home soil.

Season In The Sun

I am up here for about eight weeks. I started at the end of June and will be going home around mid-August. But nothing is really planned. It is all very ad hoc. I am not even sure if I am formally supposed to hand my notice in and how much warning am I expected to give. Probably slightly unfair if I tell the boss on a Friday that I will be leaving on Saturday. It has never really been discussed or put in any terms and conditions.

That is what I like about this job. It is all very informal. No set hours, no set travel, no clocking on and off, no reporting. The only rule is, sell as much ice cream as you can. Being on commission is a rather large if not a huge incentive. To be honest I hardly ever think about it that much. I have no set career path after this, other than avoid anything to do with accounting, banking or anything else vaguely monetary. To me money doesn't talk, it swears, and I have no idea how to deal with it. My only claim to fame comes from the other side when, by some simple twist of fate or divine destiny, I actually finished top in English at school one year. My classmates were so shocked, and probably the teachers too, that smelling salts were passed round.

Full credit to my teacher, Cracker Robinson as was affectionately called, for giving me the chance to enjoy words. His attitude was simply if you don't want to learn and listen, just sit at the back and try not make too much noise. I was hooked and sat at the front. He was so passionate about his subject that it was only fair, and a privilege, to be part of it. I even asked questions, read out aloud and took it all in. There was none of "well you tell me" nonsense.

That was then. I am very much stuck in the here and now. Here is Seahouses and all surrounding areas and now is all about cashing in on cones and making a bit of money.

Sometimes I have to pinch myself. This really is turning into a dream job. Go where I like and when I like. Read a book, have a coffee, listen to the radio, hustling at the harbour, cruising along to Craster or being bound for Bamburgh. So many options, so many choices and they are all mine.

I haven't really travelled far yet. Born, raised and educated in Newcastle. Summer holidays in either Northumberland or Scotland. Having Scottish parents meant lots of journeys back to their homeland, either to see and stay with relatives or visit several parts in the family caravan.

I have been hugely fortunate. Such a great childhood and as far as I am concerned, it is still continuing—just about to leave my teenage years behind—with the road to maturity ahead. It could be a long and winding road so plenty of time to think about that as the year's progress. But not today.

Again, as I wake up, the sun is shining. I

can't remember the last time it rained. To be honest, endless sunshine can be monotonous. It is not really the British way of life. We do like a bit of variation in the weather. Also, if the heavens did open, I would have the perfect excuse to take it easy. Park the van somewhere off the beaten track, turn the radio on and get that book out. No customers today please. Just the odd rainy day now and then would be fine.

But no, the temperatures just seem to keep on rising every day without a break. It is like new records being continually set and then broken. Still, being an ice cream man, it really is bonanza time, I have hit the jackpot. This, as I may have already mentioned, is turning into the hottest of hot summers.

Northumberland has never been known for its Mediterranean climate. More precipitation than parasols. Windy and wet rather than warm. Well, that is the common conception and far from the real story. Yes, we do have our unfair slice of the climate cake when it comes to everyday weather but far from the negative press normally directed towards this part of the world. The preconception of inclement weather tends to come from people who have never been here or from the locals who don't want too many visitors.

As stated, Northumberland does compare favourably with its southern rivals of Devon and Cornwall, it is just less talked about. Indeed, Northumberland is very often by-passed by travellers on their way to Edinburgh and then maybe the glorious wild lands of the Highlands.

It is often stated that Northumberland, and the coast in particular, is a well-kept secret as far as desirable holiday destinations are concerned. We have castles around virtually every corner, miles and miles of golden sands, lots of history and heritage. Just don't tell anyone please.

To be fair, it does seem the word on the streets has not got out yet. It has barely turned nine in the morning but there are a lot of people about already. As I arrive In

Seahouses for another day there is a sense of expectancy and excitement in the air. The gift shop that never closes has already blocked the pavement with beach balls and buckets, the Milk Bar has a few early customers and there are some early birds making their way to the sands or wandering round the harbour to catch a glimpse of the returning fishing boats and their catches.

I do notice, as I have almost every day, that the accents remain the same. Most people have ventured up here from Newcastle or from the southern parts of Scotland. When I serve someone with an accent as broad as Geoff Boycott and as liquid as Tetley's bitter, I always feel as though I have stumbled across someone from foreign parts. Then again, maybe Yorkshire is miles away in both culture and sound, but they are fiercely loyal of the land of their birth. It always reminds me of the tale when God was spotted walking around the White Rose County and asked what he was doing. He replied: "Working from home."

They are proud of their heritage, and I do like them. What you see is what you get as they say. Sometimes it might be helpful if they didn't keep mentioning just how great Yorkshire is all the time. It is a fine part of the world, but we don't need to be constantly reminded.

Northumberland people tend to be more reticent. Just happy and lucky to live here and keep quiet about just how great it is. Though a little more immodesty might be a step forward. I always get the impression that Northumberland likes to welcome visitors but is just as happy when they go home.

I have to say I have been here in the winter and it is marvelous. A walk on Bamburgh beach, the cold wind howling in the bones of your face and the castle proudly guarding over you, is simply wonderful. A completely different scenario to what I am seeing today. I like both the seasonal settings. I am a man, or teenage boy, for all seasons.

It is great to be here now. The sun shining,

the ice cream chimes about to chime and the Monkey Blood all set to flow.

The morning catch-up is as entertaining and welcoming ever. I guess I am about halfway through my summer sentence and well into the swing of things now. This is about the only routine part of the job and strangely it is good to have some sort of set pattern.

Conversation flows as fast as the Monkey Blood will be later.

"Morning Rern. How are you today? Get up to much last night?"

"No, by the time I finished at the caravan sites it was almost getting dark. There seem to be a lot of people around at the moment."

"Yes, tell me about it. We are probably reaching the peak of the season. Make the most of it. It won't be long until everyone has gone back home."

"Great. I am really enjoying it though. The harbour at Beadnell is still my favourite spot. The scenery is always changing. I saw a couple

of those metal detectorists again yesterday, if that is what you call them. I have no idea why they do it. Can't expect they find anything apart from a few cans and the odd dropped coined. Not exactly a treasure trove."

"Aye, true enough Rern. But just think if they do find something really valuable. Then you won't see them again. They will living the high life in some fancy villa in Spain. Personally, I am happy just selling a bit of pop. It keeps me going."

"So you didn't sell much ice cream yesterday?"

"No, but you bugger I sold some pop."

"Heh, we got there in the end lads. Come on let's get a cup of coffee before hitting the road. Can't keep our customers waiting."

The van is well stocked. A couple of churns of ice cream, assorted lollies and a stack of cones almost as high as the Empire State building. Ready for the off.

For a second, I wander about venturing somewhere different. But I suppose I have covered all the likely spots. Might be worth venturing into Embleton to see if anyone is awake yet. Surely, they can't sleep all the time. There must be some living souls around. No, I will leave the good people of Embleton to their soporific life. The chimes might wake them up and scare them.

No, today, it is off back to the harbour. The van ambles along quite nicely as I leave Seahouses. There are already a few golfers on the course. I really must have a proper go at that sometime. Hitting a stationary ball can't be that difficult.

I am more used to the oval shaped rugby ball having played the game throughout my school days and look forward to continuing when I get to university. I love the five nation games and have been lucky enough to see Scotland at Murrayfield a few times, courtesy of my long-suffering father. He has spent hours taking me up there as well as those regular football trips to St James' Park. His home team is Dumbarton. All I know is they play at the wonderfully named Boghead, are mostly part-time and probably not very good. I have no idea what division they are in. I suspect Rangers and Celtic are not on their fixture list.

Not far from the golf course and on the other side of the road is a large collection of white bell-shaped tents. They seem to have sprung up overnight and from the sign on the gate to the field they appear to some kind of Boys' Brigade. Not entirely sure what that is but it all looks very regimented and uniformed. The tents are in a perfect symmetrical formation, a few flags here and there and the odd bit of smoke drifting up into the blue skies.

Could be a new market for me. Then again it could be some strange sort of cult and enter at your own peril. I have heard about the Moonies, a religious movement which has dubious recruitment procedures, especially for the young and the innocent, and once signed-up they are never seen again. Some guy called Sun Myung Moon is apparently the main man. Now there is a hint. It would be good fun getting his name called out for a bar meal, make a change from Captain Fantastic. I suspect it is possibly a little more sinister. Could be wrong. Who I am to judge? Still not sure if ice cream is part of their diet. Give it a miss for the time being.

The tents have been noted just in case the boss asks why I haven't approached them. Always good to do your research.

The permanent campsite appears on my right just as the white tents fade from the rear-view mirror. This is entirely innocent. Campers under varied forms, shapes and sizes of canvas for the ultimate outdoor holiday. It is a like a little village with small tents squeezed next to large ones that must take at least a week to put up. Then there are those who literally seem to have packed the kitchen sink. They have such an array of catering equipment, ranging from large stoves to tables, chairs and enough pots and pans to have emptied their permanent homes and brought them here to the beach.

I have not inspected the site from within as a sign on the gate seems to indicate I would not be welcome and there is a shop already there for the happy campers. I might go in one day just to see what happens, unless the Moonies get to me first.

From the campsite, the main road bends to the left and I enter Beadnell. My first stop as usual is the tiny shop which seems to store just about everything. I pick up a morning newspaper, maybe a loaf of bread and a pint of milk and some assorted foodstuffs just to keep me going. I drive back to my caravan, drop them off and find time for a quick cuppa and a scan of the sports pages.

After this it is back to the main Harbour Road, which has the sea on one side and a single line of mainly holiday or second homes on the other. I eye them enviously. I would like one of those please.

Two minutes later the road curves round to the right but I go straight on to a narrower road that leads down to the harbour. I pass the sailing club and get my first glimpse of the beach and the lime kilns as I eventually turn the van round. Now, the selling window faces the sands and I am ready for a quick getaway if needed.

Engine off, radio on and window open. It is already getting warm and my first customer of the day is waiting.

"Good morning. Nice day. Can I help you?"

"Yes, I was just wondering what a 66 is. Is it an upside down 99?"

"No, just a bit smaller. Would you like one?"

"It's okay. I will just have an ordinary cone please"

"Do you want Monkey Blood with that?"

I am in a good mood. Another day begins

The Beginning Of The End

This is the biggest day of the year. It is literally all hands-on deck. The big finale, the big bonanza.

It is August Bank Holiday, and it really marks the end of the summer. After this is all over, the caravanners will leave the sites, campers take their tents down and those in holiday homes will shut doors and head back to reality of everyday life. Many other places will be shutting up shop. Not the Farne Gift Shop of course, that will remain open come rain, hail or shine, winter or spring; it is the shop for all seasons. I have never checked this, but it is probably open Christmas Day for those wanting to fly a kite after the Queen's Speech or knock around with a beach ball to lose some of the calories from the enormous festive lunch.

Today is the Seahouses Lifeboat Fete. It is set in stone in the calendar as the one and only chance to raise as much money as possible for the Royal National Lifeboat Institution and help ensure that Seahouses will always have a lifeboat, and everyone round here will be safe at sea.

It is a fantastic charity with men and women giving up their day jobs at only seconds notice to launch themselves in aid of those who may be in peril on the sea. More often than not, they are putting their own lives at risk to save the lives of others as they crash into the raging waves. Those in need range from floundering fishing boats to those who have fallen asleep on their inflatable lilos and drifted nearer to Norway than the Northumberland coast.

The saving lives at sea charity was founded in 1824 under the rather cumbersome title Royal National Institution for the Preservation of Lives at Sea and Property from Shipwreck. Some thirty years later it was given the more friendly title of Royal National Lifeboat Institution and still goes by that name today.

During the two world wars, crews saved

more than 12,000 lives; they were involved in Operation Dynamo with the evacuation of the Dunkirk beaches in 1940.

Of course, things would have been that much different in the past. The present lifeboat is a state-of-the-art high-powered machine with all the latest technology that can locate mackerel five miles away, never mind a broken-down vessel or a stranded swimmer. It can be launched in seconds and seeing it splash into the harbour and set-off is an inspirational moment. The crew, clad in yellow, look like an army on the move. The battle is on to beat the sea.

The fete is a wonderful way to say thank you to all the crews and other volunteers who run the station in Seahouses and keep the lifeboat ship shape and ready to go. There are flags and stalls everywhere and the crowds come in their thousands. You have to get in early to get a parking space, be prepared to queue for your fish and chips and come armed with coins to throwaway in the amusements.

Everyone is geared up for the big day. Shops are well stocked, restaurants and pubs with extra staff, tea towels with Puffins piled up and kites ready for take-off. For me, it really is big business. My last chance to rake in a few pennies and keep the customers, and the boss of course, satisfied. Today, it helps that the sun is still shining. It is like a military operation in the ice cream world. Jonny in the shed, or the factory as we like to call it, is churning out the ice cream on an industrial scale. Extra chocolate flakes have been bought in, the cones and wafers are on stand-by. We are under starter's orders for the final race. The jackpot bonanza, where the going is set to be good.

First recorded details show the 1852 lifeboat here, was a self-righting boat, 30 feet in length and powered by ten men with oars. Of course, our very own Grace Darling showed it was not a male dominated world when she carried her rescue in 1838 and got there before the lifeboat crews arrived.

Volunteer lifeboat crews have saved thousands of lives around the country for nearly 200 years. This day just seems the appropriate moment to say thank you. We have had our fun by the seaside in Beadnell, Bamburgh, Seahouses and Craster this summer and having you guys around has always made us feel safe.

But it also tinged with sadness. I know this is it. The end of a carefree summer. Sunshine, sand and sales. Music, sport and reading. A lot of laughs and fun along the way. This is the final curtain, the big ending, the final twist in a gloriously happy plot, "*you bugger I have sold some pop,*" turned those 99's upside down, tasted the odd kipper or two, countless portions of chips and fish, and the odd pint or two with the locals.

My day starts slightly early. I even had an early night in preparation. We are going over the top today and have to be ready. Arriving at command centre at Seahouses and I can already see things are a little bit different. Frank and Tommy are well ahead of schedule. White jackets on, crates of soft drinks loaded and their vans looking incredibly clean.

I have a bit of catching-up to do. But I did think ahead last night, finished slightly earlier in order to be one step in front for the big day. I scrubbed the van inside and out, threw away any rubbish, cleaned the windows and even did a quick stock take on how many cones and wafers I had.

But today the boxes and cartons are everywhere. You can't move for supplies. Everyone is here. No one is really talking. The usual banter is not there. This is looking serious. Even the boss is looking a little nervous. This is his big pay day as well. After this, sales will slump, and the vans will soon be back in the garage until next year. It is a short season and a long winter.

He greets me with a jolly "good morning" and asks if everything is alright.

"*Let's get ready as quickly as possible and*

get out there. It is going to be really busy. Look at the car parks. They are already filling up. Let's do our best again guys. Really big effort please."

"Jonny is on hand all day. As soon as you run out of ice cream, just hurry back and get some more. This is it. The big push. The big day. The one we have been preparing for. Let's get out there and get at them. Good luck."

All the vans are lined up in formation like that invading army of tanks ready for the final push. It is all very exciting. Even the shops have opened early, the man in the amusement arcade is already in place, the gift shop is overflowing with beach balls, spades, kites and other assorted paraphernalia. In fact, outside the shop you can't even see the pavement. God knows what it is like inside. Probably even more chaotic than usual. I get the impression that some of the staff have been up all night stacking the shelves in that random throwaway fashion. Who knows where all the items have landed.

Once again, the sun is already blazing down and the temperatures are up. It should be some finale. There is definitely an end of term party feel about the whole place. It is just about the last day of the summer holidays. Tomorrow most people will be back home, back at work or getting ready for school. This really is the final curtain. Regrets, I've had a few, too few too mention. But through it all, I did it my way.

I think some of the prices have been changed. It looks as though the 66's may be a little bit dearer today. That is not going to keep sailing club man happy. But heh ho. Make hay while the sun shines and all that. Summer will soon be gone. The ice cream is rising to the top. Cones will be going out like confetti. No wafer-thin wages today.

Seahouses may be the epicentre of the fete, but tremors can be felt as far afield as Bamburgh, Beadnell and all surrounding areas. There are people everywhere. So, my plan today is slightly different.

I warm up with my usual spot by the harbour at Beadnell. My customers will be expecting me. I can't let them down today. So, I stay here all through late morning, across lunch and then nip on to the side of the road near the golf course and entrance to Seahouses.

Bang, business is booming. In no time at all I have no ice cream left. Time for a quick reload. Even after a reload there is no time to set off as the clammer for ice cream shows no sign of abating. I stay in Seahouses for a while. This is where the crowds are beginning to build and my colleagues need help. All hands to pump. This is our biggest scoop.

The place is packed. I have never seen it so busy. Looking down to the harbour is just a swarming mass of humans of all shapes and sizes. Prams and pedestrians. People and pandemonium. But all quite orderly. The stalls, for a variety of charities and causes alongside the RNLI are all doing great business and the lifeboat crew are giving some lucky ones the chance to set out to sea on board the latest technology. It is a real carnival atmosphere.

But I can't stay here all day. I really should get back to Beadnell. The harbour will also be busy today. I know there is some kind of regatta taking place. Scores of tiny dinghies racing one another, although I am not entirely sure what the course is or how they work out who wins. There are lots of flags flying at the sailing club, lots of serious looking people in ties and blazers, clutching clipboards and blowing whistles. All seems a bit chaotic, but I am sure there is method in their madness. They know what is happening, when the races start and when they finish. They will be handing out the trophies to the winners and no doubt drinking long into the night. More importantly it means there will be even more people around than usual. More ice creams to sell. More customers to satisfy. More money to be made. I have to get back there.

Even leaving Seahouses is difficult. There

are cars parked everywhere. I stop a couple more times along the way as it is just too good an opportunity to miss. Business is brisk but not for long, I need to get back to the harbour, the regatta and the general frenzy around the old place. The lime kilns may even be buckling and listing under the pressure.

Getting back to my favourite spot is like an achievement in itself. I have to navigate my way around even more parked cars, avoid people walking on the roads and drive even slower than normal.

Reaching the harbour feels as though as I am an emergency service. Everyone gets out of my way to make sure I can park safely and then, even before I have turned the engine off, the queues are already forming. This is going to be really busy. I just hope I have enough churns to cope. Having to return to base will be another nightmare journey and I will leave a lot of desperate people behind, desperate for that one last ice cream before the holidays are finished. It is like the perfect ending to their seaside experience. For me it is my last big shift, my final push, the big farewell.

It is also a bit emotional. Many of the people I see today I have come to know during the last few weeks. Not exactly friends. I don't know many, if any, by name, but I can certainly recognise them. I know the ones always have plain cones, the others who go for 99's and those who just want to chat. With queues stretching nearly all the way to Scotland the most popular question of the day is *"have you been busy?"* Now I know how a taxi driver feels. I like small chat but there are limits.

The people just keep coming. The queue just gets longer and longer. Everyone wants an ice cream today. It is just great fun. My back has never bent so much in one day and the Monkey Blood has never flowed so quickly. But I am pleased to see the fun flavouring all goes very quickly. There is no more. But no one seems to mind. The carnival atmosphere gets even more upbeat. Blue skies, boats everywhere on the sea, beach nomads on their last lap and even some new customers. Those just up here for the day. Personally, if I was a day tripper, I would choose a quieter day. Yes, there is plenty to see and do, not that much space to do it in. Come back when the crowds don't camouflage the scenery. You won't have to wait as long for an ice cream and they will be cheaper.

Right, as the queues eventually thin out, it is time for one last victory lap of the caravan sites. Everyone seems to have had a good day. Lots of the people are wearing RNLI stickers or carrying assorted RNLI goodies. Good on them. They have donated. The crews deserve it.

Again, I know the crowds will not be the same again after this. Bank Holiday is the big banker. Tomorrow will be much slimmer pickings, just the bare bones to scavenge on. All the meat will have gone. Still, it is great fun going round my flakey friends on a final circuit. I do make a special effort to ask everyone if they have enjoyed the summer, will they be back next year. As my own little thank you, I do give out bigger portions, stick to the old prices and dish out my remaining chocolate flakes like loyalty cards. They have been great. Coming every night to get scoop after scoop from the churns. Sticking with me rather than moustached man, who has been strangely conspicuous by his absence in recent days. He has thrown in the towel, accepted defeat and exited left gracefully. No handshakes or even milkshakes. I would have gladly offered the hand of friendship. It has been a long season and there are no hard feelings. He just needs to trim that moustache, lower the fist and have happier thoughts for next time around. It is only ice cream after all.

This really is a wonderful part of the world. Castles, cones, chips, caravans and coast. Puffins and people. Beaches and beauty spots. Spectacular.

Not a bad place to spend a summer. I will miss it. Well not everything. I won't miss Monkey Blood. Red mush disguised as flavouring. Why it is so popular I will never know. These last few weeks, I suppose, have been all about Monkey Blood, sweat and beers, with the odd 66, nougat wafer or bottle of pop thrown in for good measure.

The seaside is special. Especially special around here. You always feel better with the breath of sea air in the lungs. Refreshing and exhilarating and just some of the best medicine around. A few gulps of sea air and you feel cleansed, healthy and ready to go. The batteries recharged, the motor running and health and wellbeing restored. It is like a top up on life itself. Even watching the tide go in and out is a special moment. All to do with the moon. That is as far as I know. But there again I have no idea how a radio or a telephone works.

I am happy with the sound of the sea and the seagulls. It is like looking at the stars at night. How does it all work? Is there life on Mars? How did man get to the moon? But you know what? I don't really care. At this precise moment it just seems to all make sense. But there again, I am slightly bias. This has been my home for the last few weeks. And I do feel at home here.

Of course it all helps when you can make a few bob out of it and have fun along the way.

I am beginning to feel a little tired as I finally exit the sites. Suddenly my back is beginning to ache, the odd muscle here and there is stretched and my right hand appears to be in the perfect shape of a scoop. I stop just to have a quick tidy up, remove the wooden tray to one side and try and put the piles of notes in some kind of sensible stack. I must have made record sales today. The boss will be happy. I am happy. I know the final whistle will be sounding soon. Some people are still on the caravan site. They think it's all over. It is now.

The Final Curtain

The bunting is down, the crowds have disappeared. The blinds are down on the caravans, the dinghies are back on dry land and the dogs are having their last walks on the beach.

It almost seems rude to interrupt proceedings. Having an ice cream now would just remind people of those long summer days, the carefree calories, the everlasting sunshine and faraway islands.

This is the day after the big day. From lifeboats to life changing in so many ways. It seems this glorious part of world, has already been fitted out for its winter coat. The hats and scarves are ready and the people around here, the locals, will soon have the place back to themselves. My van will be joining them in storage for another year, left in the corner of the yard, locked up and taking a deep breath after one of the longest and hottest summers ever. It deserves a rest. Whether it will have enough energy to take the roads again next year, 1977, is a question for another day.

I know how the old van feels. I could do with a rest. My work here is nearly done and I have hardly enough energy myself to see it through. But one last effort is needed and here I am loading up for another day. It just doesn't feel the same. The sun seems to have set already.

There are only a couple of us in today. Me and "you bugger I sold some pop". He still has his communities to serve. For me it is all a bit somber, tired and forlorn. The high-octane febrile excitement of yesterday has dissipated in an unwelcoming cloud of reality. This is it. We are way passed the peak. The only way is down.

Even Seahouses looks a bit tatty this morning. Shredded papers, cans and crumpled flags are rolling down the street like tumbleweed. It must have been some party. I half-expect to see the lifeboat washed up on the roundabout, revellers reclining on the pavements, and everything closed. Even the seagulls are quiet.

But there is life after all. The gift shop is open of course. The last beacon of light in this fast-fading summer. Beach balls and bucket and spades still formed up outside as a last guard of honour to the holiday season. There don't look to be many people interested or up for a good time today. The good times have gone. All those gifts from the gift shop that keeps on giving are now in the boots of family cars, tucked away under caravans or just simply shredded and cast aside. No longer needed. How many kites have been sold this summer I wonder? How many have made more than just a maiden flight? I can only guess it has been a bumper summer for the most chaotic of gift shops. I really do believe it never closes. Maybe Santa pops in on Christmas Day to pick up some last-minute goodies for the excited youngsters, though he probably gives the kites a quick swerve. Sleigh bells rather than chimes and carols replacing cones.

It is all a bit half-hearted today. I am still shattered from the marathon of yesterday and this feels a bit like extra time that nobody really wants at the end of a stamina sapping cup final.

This is it. The final farewell. My last day as an ice cream man. But you wouldn't really know it. There is no big ceremony. No big thank-you card. No party. No big send-off. It is time to say goodbye to the gang as we have our last brew together.

Jimmy, Mr Bamburgh himself is immaculately turned out as usual. It could just be my poor eyesight or the really bright early morning sunshine, but his white coat seems even whiter than usual. I didn't actually know such a bright shade existed. Maybe he has put some extra gloss on this morning as a final nod to me, that he is the one who sets the standards.

He is quiet and hushed and every word is one of wisdom.

"*So this is it son. Your last day. Make the*

most of it as the sun is still shining and we are looking set for another hot one. Your last chance to make a few pennies."

"It is. But it has been fun. When I come back next time, I am going to set up in Bamburgh. Can't have all the best spots to yourself."

At this point a small scowl emerges across his poker like face as if to say, *"don't think about it son."*

He knows I am only joking.

"Rern I know you wouldn't do that. You seemed to have made Beadnell your territory. Have a good one. It has been good meeting you and I hope you have enjoyed working with us. We are a pretty harmless bunch."

"I have a few weeks left yet. Few regulars to go round and Bamburgh is still quite busy. But then I am looking forward to a nice, quiet winter before starting up again next year if I am still up to it."

"Thanks Jimmy you have been a friend indeed and a friend in need. Your guidance and good company have been appreciated. It

would be good if we all meet up again next summer."

Then "*you bugger I sold some pop*" chimes in.

"*Aye Rern. All the very best. I have to get off soon. Plenty of bottles of pop on board. Off round the villages again. Like Jimmy I'll be around for a few weeks yet. Look after yourself.*"

And that's about as emotional as it gets round here. What you see is what you get. No need to use fifty words when ten will get to the point. I just hope I have fitted in. There have been no problems, no arguments, no animosity. All very friendly and good natured. I will miss these guys.

Then it is up the wooden stairs one more time to collect my churns from the ever-cheerful Jonny. I am tempted to ask for the ice cream recipe, but I would probably have more luck asking him to split the atom.

I collect just one churn from the factory. More than enough for today. Jonny hands it over as though it's some unexpected loose change he has found in his pocket. There is a little bit of bounce left.

"There you go. One more churn for Rern. You must have emptied a few of these this summer. See it is my magic recipe. All down to me. It is being that good that makes it easy to sell. I amaze even myself at times. Careful with it. Don't suppose you will be needing more. Not many people around today."

"It's been fun. See you around... So how do you make it Jonny. You can tell me. It is my last day. Your secret is safe with me."

"Bugger erf Rern"

And that is it. The final words. The final chapter. The boss does make a fleeting appearance.

"Make sure your van is clean and tidy when you are finished. Here's your float. Have a good day. See you later."

No big speeches then, no presentations, no fuss. This is why I like this job and this place so much.

I drive out of Seahouses for the final lap and onto the well-worn track to Beadnell. I will just stay at the harbour all day and soak it all in. I am not even going to bother with the caravan sites. It would be like going to an empty theatre when you have been playing to full houses all year. I just want to remember them at their bustling best.

The harbour is quiet with just the occasional person about, the very last of the holidaymakers, the ones staying until the final curtain. Again, the sun is cracking the lime kilns and simmering off the sea with the sands looking a little sunburned. I do a feel a touch of sadness. It would have been far better to go out with the audience shouting for more. Not today though. It is going to be the quietest of exits.

The boxes of cones are piled up in one last stand, the cans of soft drinking are almost too shy to come out and the even the flakes have gone into hiding. One day was always going to my last day and I really wasn't expecting a big send-off.

I am even slightly nervous that the van won't start. Maybe my old friend and faithful companion has also had enough. Turning on the engine seems a step too far, but it does flicker into action as I trundle off back down the coast to Beadnell.

There are a couple of families on the beach giving their assorted paraphernalia one last airing before being stored away in the long, cold and dark months ahead. I can see three or four dogs bounding along near the shore and even one little child trying to fly a kite. I feel like running across and saying *"Forget it, it will never take-off. Tell your mum and friends to come and get an ice cream."*

The sight of the kite is a fitting finale to my last shift. *"Nice day but no chance of lift-off."* Surprisingly, I do get a couple of early customers who just want a cone each and a couple of guys in search of soft drinks.

I think of the queues of the people I have

served over the weeks. The sailing fraternity, the beach dwellers, the dog walkers, the walkers and the day trippers. A mixed bunch but very loyal. They have helped me pay for a few fish and chip meals and a few beers with enough put aside in savings to add just a little to my tiny bank balance.

The fishermen have long returned from their early morning catches and some are sitting in the lime kilns or next to the boats and fixing a few lobster pots, untangling bits of rope and having merry banter with the few that are passing.

Their little wooden shed, which nestles just around the corner from the kilns, seems well stacked with everything to do with fishing and added extras. Piles of those pots, buoys, rope and, I am only guessing here, kettles for endless cups of tea and cans of beer. I have never actually been inside the shed, it's very much a member only type of place and you need your sea skills to be allowed in. I suspect to get in the shed, you have to knock and a little sliding panel opens. You are then asked a series of questions to make sure you know one end of a lobster pot from another.

Lobsters, with their long bodies and huge muscular tails, have never enticed me as a seafood delicacy. They must be hugely difficult to dissect, and I have no idea what they taste like. All I know is they attract huge prices and cost a lot when they are on the menu. It is the same with mussels. When you see people eating them in a restaurant they end up with messy fingers and a table that looks like a giant Meccano set has just toppled over. All that effort into eating them seems fairly futile. You will end up hungrier than when you first started.

Lobster pots are quite ingenious in their simplicity and they do not seem to harm their intended victims. I am told the lobster is attracted with bait through an entrance called a head. This innocently leads into the "kitchen" where a larger bait is conveniently located. Then when the lobster has taken the bait, salted mackerel or the like, and tries to leave, there is no way out. It is caught in a trap which is a funnel shaped net that leaves them stuck in the "bedroom." Next stop is the menu.

Still, each to their own. I might try lobster one day. For the moment I am always intrigued to see them landed along with the crates loaded with crabs. I have a high respect for the fishermen. It is a tough job. Out in all weathers and never really sure if you are catching enough to make ends meet. But they always seem the healthiest people in the world with remarkably rugged and bronzed faces. They are always good for a chat even though the burr is sometimes difficult to understand. I do give them the occasional free ice cream. It seems the least I can do.

I can tell this is going to be a really slow day, by a long stretch the slowest of the summer. Custom is a mere trickle, and I will be shutting up shop early. Not immediately as I notice the wooden money tray is looking particularly bereft. There are a few coins and a couple of five-pound notes and that is about it. Need to get it in better shape before the end of play.

My company today is mainly the radio and there is not much happening there either. No sport, no comedy or interesting documentaries, so I have to be content with a bit of music. Even that sounds tired and faded. Summer really is fading out fast. Even the seagulls seem to have taken the day off and had a lie in.

The few people on the beach are also leaving early. Maybe this is their last time and it is off to pack away their belongings and their memories of a golden summer and make their weary way back home. I feel like having a large banner saying "Closing Down Sale. Everything Must Go" and just giving everything away at ridiculously low prices or just entirely free. I know I will be giving bigger portions today. Just my way of saying "thanks guys, it's been fun."

No rush today. Yes, my 66's will be as big as 99's and the Monkey Blood will be in flow for the last time. I don't really care. It is a bit of an empty feeling. I wish I had just finished yesterday and gone out with a bang.

But no, the show must go on even if many of the seats are empty. I do feel a sense of duty. For my boss the prospect of a bleak winter is already on the horizon. No one will want a nougat wafer or single cone in December. This is the last chance to make a bit of money for us all. It is a short season and a long break.

I know the Lifeboat Day signals the end of my days here but in reality, the countdown began midway through August. This is when the annual Community Shield match between the Division One champions and FA Cup winners is played at Wembley.

This year it was Liverpool and second division Southampton who lined-up against each other. For the record it was a one-nil victory for the Merseysiders with Kevin Keegan nodding down for John Toshack to score the only goal of the game in the 50th minute. It was played in front of a crowd of 76,500.

It is seen as the curtain-raiser to the new

season and for me it is the first sign that summer will be soon ebbing away as quickly as the tide and the floodlights will be switched on and the football pitches cleared of snow. The radio commentary just reminds me that my days up here are numbered.

So here I am on the last lap. My mind begins to wonder to the land of numbers. How many people have I served? How much ice cream have I sold? How many 66's? How many 99's? How much money have I made?

So many questions but not many answers. Strangely the first few are quite entertaining and keep me occupied for a few minutes without coming up with any real figures of estimates. The truth is I really don't have a clue and it's all a little immaterial and impossible to calculate. I know I have sold enough to keep the boss happy and survived so far without the threat of dismissal. No accidents. The van has emerged unscathed through it all and there have been no disasters.

The closest I have come to controversy and upset is my brief and unwanted encounter with half-man half-walrus and not looking after my health due to a heavyweight diet of beer, fish and chips and ice cream. It is just really sad it is coming to an end.

It has all been so simple and I have been almost humbled to have been given a part in the annual summer drama. There have been no frills or grabbing centre stage and getting all the best lines. Everyone here, local or visitor, has a part to play and just gets on with it. That is the way things are done round here. No formalities, no training, no targets, no boundaries, no nonsense. Everyone, bar the odd opposition calamity and the grudging sailing fraternity, has been so friendly and welcoming. Do the job and the rest will follow.

My brothers in arms have been helpful, humorous and just general all round good guys. Their friendship, Northumbrian burr, camaraderie has been top of the league. Never a bad word between us, no clashes, no friction, no trouble. The ice cream team is a solid outfit. All for cone and all that.

It has been more than just a pleasure; it has been more of a privilege. To be here in the middle of such spectacular scenery, surrounded by history and heritage, is something never to be taken for granted. I just feel so fortunate to have been weaved into the fabric of it all in my own little way. Okay, I know it is only selling ice cream but somehow it just seems so much more than that. Something bigger. Something really special.

***

My back does ache slightly more than usual and I certainly won't miss all that bending down in a confined space, knocking my head on the roof, the long hours and all those incessant questions about 66's. But I will miss a whole bunch of other things.

The sense of freedom, the sense of fun and

the sense of just doing something you enjoy and don't really have to worry is just so satisfying. Nostalgia is not what it used to be, but when I look back it will always bring a smile.

Not quite Jack Kerouac's 'On The Road' but I do think some of the lines from the book fit in quite nicely when I reflect on it all.

"We all must admit that everything is fine and there's no need in the world to worry, and in fact we should realise what it would mean to us to understand that we're not really worried about anything."

"Never really thought I'd amount to anything. It was precisely what I wanted the whole world to think; then I could sneak in, if that's what they wanted, and sneak out again, which I did."

Maybe all a bit too deep and meaningful but sometimes good to take a step back and a have a quiet think about it all. But not for too long.

Just enjoy the moment. You know, I do like a good quote from a book or even better a Dylan verse or three.

'Crimson flames tied through my ears, rollin' high and mighty traps

Pounced with fire on flaming roads using ideas as my maps

"We'll meet on edges, soon," said I, proud 'neath heated brow

Ah, but I was so much older then, I'm younger than that now.

Half-wracked prejudice leaped forth, "rip down all hate," I screamed

Lies that life is black and white spoke from my skull, I dreamed

Romantic facts of musketeers foundationed deep, somehow

Ah, but I was so much older then, I'm younger than that now.

Yes, my guard stood hard when abstract threats too noble to neglect

Deceived me into thinking I had something

to protect

Good and bad, I define these terms quite clear, no doubt, somehow

Ah, but I was so much older then I'm younger than that now'

Yes, 'My Back Pages'—great song, great words. Apparently, he originally recorded it under the working title *Ancient Memories.* I am sure the words will make even more sense when I look back on this most glorious of glorious summers and have my own ancient memories to look back on. Especially if I am sitting with my cardigan and slippers on, boring family and friends, or anyone else who cares to listen, that I was once an ice cream man, on the Northumberland coast. It was one of the hottest summers on record.

But I am in the present and the memories are still being recorded for future reference. It is even a little unfair to start thinking of memories when the past is not yet fully in the rear-view mirror.

It may feel once again that the granite like skies are lowering, the winds are beginning to pick up and rain could be on the way. It is that kind of sad feeling. Darkness overtaking the brightness of an everlasting summer.

Now is time to switch off the radio, close down the churns, get the engine started, slide the window shut for one last time and begin to think about my final journey back to base at Seahouses. My old faithful van, my partner, my home, my office, will at last be allowed to hibernate and get the rest it so badly needs. Who knows if it will come out again. This could be the last time on the road.

Just before I start shutting down and taking stock of it all, I take a cursory glance at my surroundings, the kilns, the sea, the sands, the last days of a glorious summer, there is a knocking sound. Strange, as almost everything is turned off and packed away. Then I realise what it is. It is a sound I have heard before. I look down and there is a little girl at the window. I have to blink twice to actually see her. She has obviously walked a long way to get here and cuts a solitary figure on an almost deserted landscape. There is no one else around.

"Yes, what can I get you?"

"Can I have a 99 please?"

"Anything else?"

"No thanks"

"Do you want Monkey Blood with that?

www.blossomspringpublishing.com

Printed in Great Britain
by Amazon

15732328R00185